NATURAL ENVIRONMENT RESEAR
INSTITUTE OF GEOLOGICAL SCI
(Geological Survey and Museum)

## British Regional Geology

# The Wealden District

(FOURTH EDITION)

---

**By R. W. Gallois, B.Sc.**

*Based on previous editions by the late*
**F. H. Edmunds, M.A.**

LONDON HER MAJESTY'S STATIONERY OFFICE 1965

*The Institute of Geological Sciences*
*was formed by the*
*incorporation of the Geological Survey of Great Britain*
*and the Museum of Practical Geology*
*with Overseas Geological Surveys*
*and is a constituent body of the*
*Natural Environment Research Council*


*First published 1935*
*Fourth edition 1965*
*Third impression 1978*

ISBN 0 11 884078 9

# Foreword to Fourth Edition

When the first edition of ' The Wealden District ' was written in 1934 by the late F. H. Edmunds, little work had been done in the Weald since the middle of the 19th century and the account was chiefly based on the classic memoirs of W. Topley (on the Weald proper), A. J. Jukes-Browne (on the Cretaceous rocks) and W. Whitaker (on the Chalk and Tertiary Deposits of north Kent). Since that time most of the Wealden District has been resurveyed by Geological Survey officers and much research has been carried out both by amateur and by academic geologists. In recent years several deep exploratory boreholes for oil have added significant information concerning the structure and stratigraphy of the concealed Mesozoic and Palaeozoic rocks to that acquired earlier in the century when the Kent Coalfield was explored.

Consequently, although the original scheme has been retained as far as possible, much of the account has been re-written and many of the original illustrations have been either replaced or revised to incorporate the new information.

Numerous colleagues have assisted in the preparation of the fourth edition and in several cases have supplied notes and contributions which have formed the basis of parts of the present work. In particular, Mr. B. C. Worssam has provided the accounts on the Pliocene and on Cambering (including Fig. 16), Mr. D. A. Gray and Mr. R. A. Downing have written an account of the Water Supply of the area, and the accounts of the Coal Measures and the Chalk are based on notes supplied by Dr. E. R. Shephard-Thorn and Mr. C. J. Wood respectively. Mr. S. C. A. Holmes has edited the present account.

*An EXHIBIT illustrating the Geology and Scenery of the district described in this volume is set out on the ground floor of the Museum of Practical Geology, Exhibition Road, South Kensington, London, S.W.7.*

# Contents

# Illustrations

## Figures in Text

## Plates

## Explanation of Plates

Plate

Front Cover — Joint-controlled erosion in Chalk cliffs, Botany Bay, Margate, Kent. Vertical jointing in the Upper Chalk has been picked out by marine erosion to form rectilinear inlets and the natural arch. Frost action has broken up the upper few feet of chalk at the cliff tops. *See* p. 79. (Geological Survey Photograph No. A9935).

I. — Geological sketch-map of the Wealden District.

II. — View of the Hythe Beds escarpment from Gibbet Hill, Surrey. View eastward. Low-lying Weald Clay country is overlooked from the north by the Hythe Beds escarpment, which rises to the wooded hills above Hascombe in the centre distance. On the left, in the far distance, is part of the same escarpment culminating at Leith Hill (965 ft O.D.). *See* p. 69. (Geological Survey Photograph No. A9690).

III. A. — Rusthall Toad Rock, Denny Bottom, near Tunbridge Wells, Kent. An isolated block of Lower Tunbridge Wells Sand which has been formed by differential erosion along a more fissile, silty bed within the massive sandstones. Although the shape of the block is due to entirely natural agencies, its extreme isolation from the remainder of the outcrop is probably due to quarrying. *See* p. 74. (Geological Survey Photograph No. A9749).

B. — Hythe Beds at Coombe Quarry, near Maidstone, Kent, where hard sandy limestone (' rag ') is worked for roadstone. About 60 ft of Hythe Beds are visible, overlain by 8 ft of glauconitic clays (Sandgate Beds) which form the overburden to the main quarry face. *See* p. 32. (Geological Survey Photograph No. A8819).

IV. — Idealized landscape on the shores of the Wealden Lake. Dinosaurian reptiles were the dominant vertebrates whilst conifers, cycads, ferns and rushes made up most of the plant life.

V. — Ammonites from the Gault and Lower Greensand.

1. *Tropaeum drewi* Casey, Lower Greensand (Hythe Beds; Lower Aptian).
2. *Parahoplites maximus* Sinzow, Lower Greensand (Sandgate Beds; Upper Aptian).
3. *Douvilleiceras mammillatum* (Schlotheim), Lower Greensand (Folkestone Beds; Lower Albian).
4. *Euhoplites lautus* (Parkinson), Lower Gault (Middle Albian).
5. *Mortoniceras inflatum* (J. Sowerby), Upper Gault (Upper Albian).

Plate

VI. Some Characteristic Fossils from the Chalk.

1. *Micraster coranguinum* Leske, Upper Chalk (*coranguinum* Zone).
2. *Phymosoma koenigi* (Mantell), Upper Chalk (*coranguinum* Zone).
3. *Terebratulina lata* Etheridge, Middle Chalk (*lata* Zone).
4. *Actinocamax plenus* (Blainville), Lower Chalk (*plenus* marls).
5. *Inoceramus lamarcki* Parkinson, Middle Chalk.
6. *Marsupites testudinarius* (Schlotheim), Upper Chalk (*Marsupites* Zone).
7. *Ptychodus latissimus* Agassiz, Upper Chalk.
8. *Schloenbachia subvarians* Spath, Lower Chalk (*varians* Zone).

VII. A. Quarry in Upper Chalk, Frindsbury, Kent. Evenly-bedded chalk is worked for cement manufacture. In the centre distance a solution pipe is filled with Thanet Beds sand. *See* p. 44. (Geological Survey Photograph No. A7864).

B. Section in Lower Eocene deposits, Upnor, Kent. At the top of the face the dark clays at the base of the London Clay can be seen overlying pale-coloured, cross-bedded sands of the Woolwich Beds. The Woolwich Bottom Bed, a line of black flint pebbles, can be seen in the centre of the face at the junction of the Woolwich Beds with the underlying fine, homogenous sands of the Thanet Beds. *See* p. 47. (Geological Survey Photograph No. A7869).

VIII. Characteristic Eocene Fossils:

1. *Ostrea bellovacina* Lamarck. Thanet Beds to Blackheath Beds.
2. *Panopea intermedia* (J. Sowerby). Thanet Beds to Headon Beds.
3. *Corbula regulbiensis* Morris. Thanet Beds to Woolwich Beds.
4. *Cucullaea decussata* Parkinson. Thanet Beds to London Clay.
5. *Xanthopsis bispinosa* M^cCoy. London Clay.

6.a, b, c. *Odontaspis macrota striata* (Winkler). Thanet Beds to London Clay.

7.a, b. *Nemocardium plumsteadianum* (J. Sowerby). Thanet Beds to London Clay.

8.a, b. *Arctica morrisi* (J. de C. Sowerby). Thanet Beds to London Clay.

9. *Glycymeris brevirostris* (J. de C. Sowerby). London Clay.

IX. A. Submerged forest of Little Galley Hill, Bexhill, Sussex. Stools of trees, the remains of a Neolithic forest, are exposed at abnormally low tides. *See* p. 65. (Geological Survey Photograph No. A3359).

Plate

B. Junction of Folkestone Beds and Gault at Copt Point, Folkestone. The dark clays of the Gault form funnel-shaped slips which partly obscure the underlying pale-coloured sandstones of the Folkestone Beds. The foreshore is littered with waveworn blocks of the sandstone. *See* p. 79. (Geological Survey Photograph No. A5394).

X. A. Superficial structures in Weald Clay; at Southwater, Sussex. Sharp folds in the incompetant shales and mudstones were probably formed by valley-bulging under permafrost conditions during the Pleistocene period. *See* p. 69. (Geological Survey Photograph No. A8321).

B. Folkestone Warren landslip, Folkestone, Kent, in which rotational movement takes place along slip-planes in the Gault. This picture, taken immediately after the major 1915 slip, shows the vertical movement of the upper part of the displaced mass. In the background the Chalk forms a steep back-face. *See* p. 68. (Reproduced by courtesy of British Railways, Southern Region).

XI. A. Coombe Deposits and Dry Valley and Nailbourne Deposits at Black Rock, Brighton. The Coombe Deposits on the right of the picture consist mainly of large angular blocks of chalk and occasional sarsens of Tertiary sandstone, set in a matrix of fine chalky mud, the whole deposit being derived from the adjacent Pleistocene sea cliff (to right of section shown). This material passes laterally into finer deposits which merge (on the left of the picture) with the well-bedded flints and chalky muds of the Dry Valley and Nailbourne Deposits. *See* p. 62. (Geological Survey Photograph No. A9932).

B. Meanders in the River Cuckmere, West Dean, Sussex. In its lower reaches, between West Dean and Cuckmere Haven, the Cuckmere meanders in wide sweeps over the alluvial flat which was formerly its estuary. *See* p. 80. (Geological Survey Photograph No. A9753).

XII. A. The Medway gap in the North Downs, near Wouldham, Kent. The Chalk slopes are marked by large quarries excavated for cement manufacture. *See* p. 75. (Geological Survey Photograph No. A7876).

B. The Chalk cliffs of the Seven Sisters, from Seaford Head, Sussex. Marine erosion is rapidly cutting back into a system of valleys which drained seawards in Pleistocene times, but which are now permanently dry. The beach in the foreground is almost entirely composed of flints derived locally from the Chalk. *See* p. 79. (Geological Survey Photograph No. A9751).

Plate

XIII. A. Shingle ridges on Dungeness. Progressive stages in the development of the Ness can be traced from right to left, each ridge marking the position of a former shoreline. The flat marshland can be seen in the background. *See* p. 80. (Reproduced by courtesy of the Committee for Aerial Photography, University of Cambridge).

B. Degraded sea cliff below the Strand Gate, Winchelsea, Sussex. The alluvial meadow in the foreground marks the inner margin of the marshland which is bounded by an old line of cliffs; at this point the cliffs consist of Ashdown Sand. *See* p. 80. (Geological Survey Photograph No. A9745).

# 1. Introduction

THE Wealden District embraces the major part of the county of Kent, the whole of Sussex, the southern half of Surrey and a small part of Hampshire. The Weald proper comprises the tract of land enclosed by the North Downs, which extend from Farnham through Guildford, Wrotham and Wye to Folkestone, the South Downs, running from Petersfield through Steyning and Lewes to Beachy Head, and the Butser hills, near Petersfield and Alton. From a geological point of view, the Weald proper is continued across the Straits of Dover into the Bas Boulonnais where a semi-circle of Chalk hills forms the eastern counterpart of the Butser hills. For present purposes, the north-eastern part of Kent including the Isles of Sheppey and Thanet, and the country east of Chichester and south of the southern boundary of the Weald proper are linked with the Weald. The extent of the district is indicated on the Geological Sketch-map, Plate I.

Many workers have been attracted to the Weald since the early days of geological research, and a very large number of papers has been published dealing in particular with the geological structure and with the fossils. Among the first accounts is one concerning " some form'd stones found at Hunton, in Kent " (i.e. shells of *Paludina* from the Weald Clay), published in *Philosophical Transactions* in 1684; whilst in 1737 there appeared ' A Dissertation upon the Surface of the Earth, as delineated in a specimen of a Philosophico—Chorographical Chart of East Kent '.

The general anticlinal structure of the surface rocks of the area was known to John Farey, who in 1806 produced in the form of a diagram a geological section across the Weald. Several manuscript copies of this were made, one of which is in the possession of the Geological Survey. Farey fully appreciated the faulted nature of the ground, and had a good idea of the sequence of beds. Although later work has shown him to have been in error in some particulars, both as regards the presence of faults near the Chalk escarpments and as regards the identification of strata, the construction of this first geological section across the Weald was a remarkable achievement. The geology of the Weald is represented on William Smith's map of England, published 1815. From this map it is apparent that, except on the broadest of outlines, little was known as to the actual outcrops of beds; moreover, Smith identified the Weald Clay with his ' Oaktree Clay ' (i.e. Kimmeridge Clay) and the Lower Greensand as Portland Stone. ' County ' geological maps of Surrey, Sussex and Kent and also a geological section were produced in 1819. Farey stated on his 1806 diagram that the section was constructed in accordance with the principles formulated by Smith, with whom he was friendly: but it may well be that he had the greater knowledge of the Weald, and provided Smith with much information; it is noteworthy that his section shows a clearer appreciation of the subject than Smith seemed to possess thirteen years afterwards.

During the first half of the nineteenth century much detailed work was carried out on the structure of the district, on the nature of individual beds and on the fossils. Gideon Mantell, a doctor in practice at Lewes, examined the strata of the central part of the Weald and established their freshwater origin; he also discovered the first known fragments of the gigantic herbivorous dinosaur *Iguanodon*, and recognized the reptilian nature of the fossil remains. W. H. Fitton examined, amongst other sections, the coast exposures between Deal and Brighton and compared and correlated the strata with those of the Isle of Wight; Thomas Webster also made a close study of the beds below the Chalk. The earliest work published by Sir R. I. Murchison, Director-General of the Geological Survey, concerned the western part of the Weald; this was issued by the Geological Society in 1826.

Sir Charles Lyell worked over parts of the Weald, and refers to the district in the first edition (1833) of his *Principles of Geology*, remarking: " It must not be supposed that the anticlinal axis . . . running through the centre of the Weald is by any means so simple as is usually represented in geological sections. There are, on the contrary, a series of anticlinal and synclinal lines, which form ridges and troughs running nearly parallel to each other."

William Hopkins and P. J. Martin both elucidated many of the major structural features, and in 1841 the former recorded that much of the Wealden folding is characterized by " the beds dipping (and in many places with great rapidity) in one direction but preserving a sensible horizontality in the opposite one "; i.e. he showed that many of the folds are of the type now described as monoclinal. R. A. C. Godwin-Austen made many keen observations on the geology of Surrey; in 1856 he formulated the theory that Coal Measures were present under parts of the Wealden area, a deduction later to be proved correct.

The latter part of the nineteenth century saw a great advance in detailed knowledge and in systematized work. In 1858 the Geologists' Association was founded, and since that date many members of the Association have carried out valuable researches into Wealden geology, among outstanding contributions being papers on the Gault by F. G. H. Price (1874 and 1879) and L. F. Spath (1923) in which the foundation of the present day classification of the English Gault was established. An account of the zones of the White Chalk of the Kent and Sussex coasts (1900) by A. W. Rowe, in which evolutionary changes in the sea-urchin *Micraster* were traced, has shown how these changes can be applied to zonal work. From 1923 to the present day valuable systematic work has been carried out by the Weald Research Committee of the Association. Much of this has been incorporated in the two Geologists' Association Guides, Nos. 24 and 29, relating to the Weald. Part of Guide No. 30, The London Region, covers the Chalk and the Tertiaries of the north Kent coast. Recent work by R. Casey (1960–64), on the stratigraphy and palaeontology of the Lower Greensand, and by P. Allen (1954–62), on the Wealden, has added much to the understanding of these divisions.

Most of our knowledge of the underground structure of the Weald has been gained since the year 1890. During 1875 and 1876 two experimental boreholes were put down at Mountfield, Sussex, under the aegis of the British Association for the Advancement of Science, but the deeper of these, taken to 1,906 ft, proved little beyond an unexpectedly great thickness of Kimmeridge Clay. The first borehole to prove Godwin-Austen's deduction of the presence of coal was made at Dover in 1890, and a colliery was established there.

Deep exploratory boreholes for oil have been drilled at Ashdown Forest, Brightling, Hellingly, Henfield, Penshurst and Shalford and these boreholes have added materially to knowledge of the deep-seated structure of the Weald.

In recent years the work of the late W. V. Lewis has thrown new light on the evolution of the coast-line.

The work of the Geological Survey in the Weald commenced in the year 1855; F. Drew, C. Gould and C. Le Neve Foster between them made the primary survey of the greater part of the area, on the scale of 1 in to 1 mile, and smaller parts were mapped by W. T. Aveline, J. Hay, T. R. Polwhele, W. Boyd Dawkins and W. Topley. Maps of the whole district, on large hand-coloured sheets (now termed 'Old Series' maps) were published at intervals between 1862 and 1893.

In 1902 the first colour-printed 'New Series' map dealing with part of the Weald was produced and rather more than half of our area is now represented by sheets of this series (*see* Section 10). A considerable portion of the Weald has been mapped on the scale of 6 in to 1 mile, and manuscript copies of all these maps are available for reference in the Geological Survey Library.

Several descriptive memoirs have been issued from time to time. *The Geology of Folkestone, Rye and Romney Marsh* was written by Drew in 1864, and in 1872 W. Whitaker gave an account of the Lower London Tertiary Beds of Thanet. In 1875 the observations of the geologists who carried out the primary 1-in geological survey of the Weald were incorporated by Topley in the well-known *Geology of the Weald.* A. J. Jukes-Browne described the Upper Cretaceous rocks in some detail in a three-volume memoir, *The Cretaceous Rocks of Britain* (1901–1904), whilst the geological aspects of water supply from underground sources have been treated in memoirs arranged on a county basis.

G. W. Lamplugh and F. L. Kitchin in 1911 added to knowledge of the underground structure of Kent in a memoir dealing with the concealed rocks of the Kent coal explorations. This knowledge has been amplified by further publications on the coalfield area, notably by Lamplugh, Kitchin and J. Pringle in 1923, by H. G. Dines, R. Crookall and C. J. Stubblefield in 1933 and by Sir A. E. Trueman and the last named in 1946.

The district possesses many features of geological interest, for although the stratigraphical range of the surface outcrops is almost wholly limited to Cretaceous and Tertiary rocks, a very complete Mesozoic sequence, underlain by various Palaeozoic strata, is known from boreholes. All the rocks known are of sedimentary origin and include freshwater and marine deposits, laid down under conditions varying from those of the shore-line to deep-water. A table of formations proved to be present is given on p. 4; the complete sequence recognized has not been found at any one place.

The structure of the Weald, as shown by the rocks exposed at the surface, is that of a broad dome, or anticline, with an axis running roughly east-south-east to west-north-west through the centre of the area. Deep borings have shown that the axis of this fold coincides more or less with the axis of a large depositional trough which was active from early Jurassic to Upper Cretaceous times. The presence of this trough was claimed by A. Strahan in 1913, when

## Table of Formations known to be present in the Wealden District

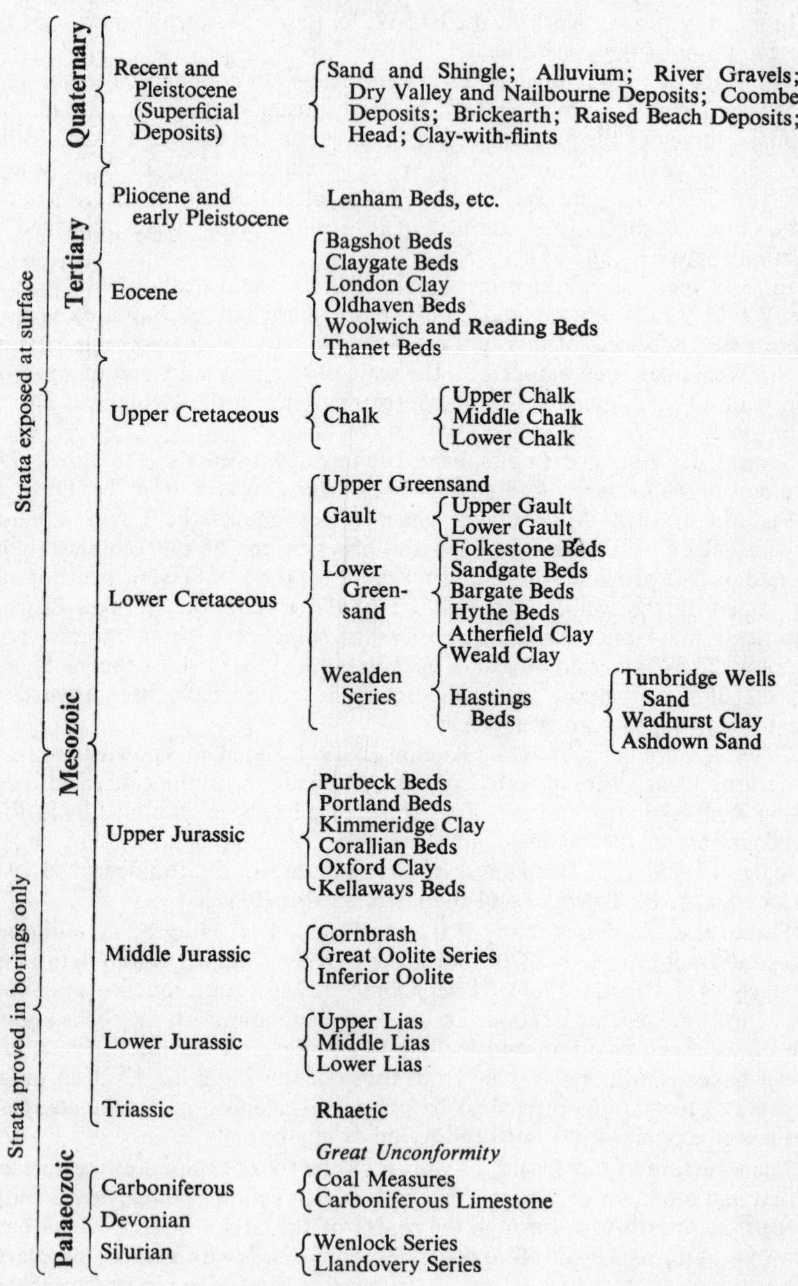

| Exposure | Era | Period | Formations | Subdivisions | Further subdivisions |
|---|---|---|---|---|---|
| Strata exposed at surface | Quaternary | Recent and Pleistocene (Superficial Deposits) | Sand and Shingle; Alluvium; River Gravels; Dry Valley and Nailbourne Deposits; Coombe Deposits; Brickearth; Raised Beach Deposits; Head; Clay-with-flints | | |
| | Tertiary | Pliocene and early Pleistocene | Lenham Beds, etc. | | |
| | | Eocene | Bagshot Beds | | |
| | | | Claygate Beds | | |
| | | | London Clay | | |
| | | | Oldhaven Beds | | |
| | | | Woolwich and Reading Beds | | |
| | | | Thanet Beds | | |
| | Mesozoic | Upper Cretaceous | Chalk | Upper Chalk | |
| | | | | Middle Chalk | |
| | | | | Lower Chalk | |
| | | Lower Cretaceous | Upper Greensand | | |
| | | | Gault | Upper Gault | |
| | | | | Lower Gault | |
| | | | Lower Greensand | Folkestone Beds | |
| | | | | Sandgate Beds | |
| | | | | Bargate Beds | |
| | | | | Hythe Beds | |
| | | | | Atherfield Clay | |
| | | | Wealden Series | Weald Clay | |
| | | | | Hastings Beds | Tunbridge Wells Sand |
| | | | | | Wadhurst Clay |
| | | | | | Ashdown Sand |
| Strata proved in borings only | | Upper Jurassic | Purbeck Beds | | |
| | | | Portland Beds | | |
| | | | Kimmeridge Clay | | |
| | | | Corallian Beds | | |
| | | | Oxford Clay | | |
| | | | Kellaways Beds | | |
| | | Middle Jurassic | Cornbrash | | |
| | | | Great Oolite Series | | |
| | | | Inferior Oolite | | |
| | | Lower Jurassic | Upper Lias | | |
| | | | Middle Lias | | |
| | | | Lower Lias | | |
| | | Triassic | Rhaetic | | |
| | | | *Great Unconformity* | | |
| | Palaeozoic | Carboniferous | Coal Measures | | |
| | | | Carboniferous Limestone | | |
| | | Devonian | | | |
| | | Silurian | Wenlock Series | | |
| | | | Llandovery Series | | |

he stated "... it appears that the sag in the Palaeozoic platform had been in progress more or less all through Mesozoic times, and that the superimposing of the Wealden Anticline upon it has been a minor incident upon the margin of the sagging area, not materially changing its character as a dominant factor in the structure of Southern England." This deduction was based upon an analysis of the known thicknesses of the outcropping Cretaceous rocks, of their present position within the anticline, and upon the results of three boreholes into the Upper Jurassic, for at that time no boring in the trough had reached the Palaeozoic floor. The exact significance of the correspondence in axial alignment between the tectonic Wealden uplift and the sedimentary Mesozoic trough is not known and the relationship may well be simply coincidental. Nevertheless, this trough was the major factor in the depositional history of the area throughout Mesozoic times as Strahan recognized.

Little is known of the detailed structure of the Palaeozoic rocks which form the sub-Mesozoic floor, except in the Kent Coalfield area where they are folded into a synclinal basin. Elsewhere it is not even possible to draw boundaries between the different systems proved.

# 2. Concealed Strata—Palaeozoic Systems

Palaeozoic rocks have been proved in every borehole which has passed through the Mesozoic cover in the Wealden area and it is inferred that some of these rocks are present everywhere beneath the area. Details of the nature and position of the folds affecting these Palaeozoic rocks are known only in east Kent, where numerous trial borings for coal and the working of coal seams have provided detailed information about the structures present. Elsewhere beneath the Weald there is only sufficient evidence to compare these rocks with other regions and, by analogy, to deduce their geological history.

The oldest rocks known in the area are of Silurian age and were deposited in deep-water marine conditions which became progressively shallower as the basin of deposition filled with sediment. Although there is no direct evidence within the Wealden District of an unconformity between the Silurian and Devonian strata, the Caledonian earth-movements, which affected the whole of north-western Europe, must have transformed much of the Silurian basin into mountain chains which provided the coarse terrestrial and deltaic sediments of the Old Red Sandstone, formed under arid or semi-arid conditions. Beneath the North Downs and east Kent, Devonian rocks are chiefly of a continental facies and probably pass southwards into marine deposits similar to those of Devon and Cornwall. Steady denudation of the hills occupying the northern part of the Wealden District occurred throughout Devonian times until they were finally inundated by a shallow shelf sea in early Carboniferous Limestone times. Minor earth-movements caused the area to be raised above sea level during the Namurian epoch, only to be submerged again by the Upper Carboniferous coal swamps which stretched from South Wales to Belgium and Holland and beyond.

In late Carboniferous and early Permian times the whole of southern England was converted into a mountainous area by the Hercynian earth-movements and it was during this period of folding that the Kent Coalfield syncline was formed. There is no evidence of the continental Permian deposits which mark the end of the Palaeozoic era and it is thought that, during this and the ensuing Triassic period, the Hercynian mountain chains were reduced to a peneplain by sub-aerial denudation. In early Jurassic times the transgressive Liassic sea spread across large areas of this peneplain and subsidence of the Palaeozoic floor, centered about an east-west axis running through the central Weald, continued until the end of the Cretaceous period, by which time parts of this floor were over 9000 ft below sea-level. During the Tertiary Alpine orogeny the Wealden uplift developed and the greatest proved depth of the sub-Mesozoic floor at the present day is −5225 ft O.D. (i.e. 5225 ft below Ordnance Datum) at Shalford.

Beneath London, the Thames estuary and east Kent Palaeozoic rocks form an almost flat platform, at about −1000 ft O.D. This is separated from the central part of the sedimentary basin, where they lie at −4000 ft O.D. to −5000 ft O.D. beneath the western Weald, by a more steeply inclined shelf passing beneath Croydon, Maidstone and Folkestone.

## Silurian System

Silurian rocks have been proved in four boreholes and consist in each of banded grey mudstones and siltstones. They are commonly stained red, purple or green and show signs of weathering for 10 to 20 feet below the contact with the beds above. The oldest proved Silurian occurs at Chilham at −1005 ft O.D. and contains graptolites, for example *Monograptus crispus*, *M. marri*, *M. nudus* and *Rastrites equidistans*, indicating the Zone of *Monograptus crispus* of the Upper Llandovery Series. Upper Llandovery rocks also occur at Shalford, at −5470 ft O.D., and contain *M.* cf. *distans* and brachiopods including *Stricklandia*. Beds of Wenlock age, containing *Atrypa reticularis* and *Leangella segmentum*, occur at −1027 ft O.D. at Cliffe; at Bobbing mudstones from −1070 ft O.D., which may be Wenlock or even Upper Llandovery in age, have yielded *Chonetes* cf. *novascoticus* and a small fragment of the trilobite *Homalonotus*.

## Devonian System

Two distinct facies of Devonian rocks are present in the area.

Red and greenish grey micaceous sandstones and conglomerate bands occur at Harmansole, at −1075 ft O.D., and at Herne at −1087 ft O.D. The presence of angular pebbles, ripple marks and rain pitting and the occurrence of the crustacean *Euestheria*, suggests that these rocks were deposited in brackish, shallow water. Plant fragments and fish scales add to the similarity between these beds and the Old Red Sandstone of the Anglo-Welsh area.

At Brightling marine Lower Devonian, comparable with that of Devon, occurs at −3837 ft O.D. and consists of chocolate coloured shales, thin micaceous sandstones and mudstones containing *Chonetes* cf. *sarcinulatus*, *Pterinea*, *Actinopterella* and *Tentaculites*. There is evidence that Upper Devonian sediments occur in the north-west of the Kent Coalfield.

## Carboniferous System

### Carboniferous Limestone

Carboniferous Limestone occurs under east Kent in an area bounded by an arc extending from Pegwell Bay through Canterbury to Hythe; it has also been proved in boreholes at Penshurst (at −4518 ft O.D.), Henfield (−5025 ft O.D.) and Shalford (−5225 ft O.D.). Two distinct divisions are recognized; a well-marked Lower Limestone Shale division, consisting of 26 ft of dark shales with thin bands of limestone crowded with crinoid ossicles and brachiopod shells, occurs at Harmansole at −1050 ft O.D. An upper Main limestone division has been proved in a number of boreholes in the Kent Coalfield. Most of the faunal zones of the Tournaisian and Viséan Stages are represented although the boreholes have not invariably entered the Carboniferous Limestone at the same horizons and no single borehole shews the complete succession. The limestone is massive and crystalline, though marl partings and oolites may occur; it contains typical Carboniferous Limestone fossils which include the brachiopod *Linoproductus corrugatohemisphericus*, corals such as *Carcinophyllum vaughani* and *Lithostrotion martini* and a few lamellibranchs.

The overstep of the Coal Measures across the Carboniferous Limestone and on to older rocks in the Kent Coalfield indicates that folding and erosion took place in the intervening Namurian times and no deposits of this age are known from the Wealden area.

**Coal Measures**

The Coal Measures of the concealed east Kent Coalfield lie at the north-western end of a synclinal basin, the axis of which trends north-west by west. This syncline lies beneath the northern limb of the anticline of Mesozoic rocks under which the undulating, eroded upper surface of the Coal Measures slopes generally to the south-west; near Deal it has been encountered at about −800 ft O.D., while at Folkestone it occurs at depths below −1300 ft O.D. The deepest known parts of the basin lie around Waldershare and St. Margaret's Bay (where the Coal Measures rest on Carboniferous Limestone at depths below −3800 ft O.D.) and a continuation of it extends beneath the English Channel. A maximum thickness of about 2900 ft of Coal Measures has been proved; they rest upon a denuded surface of the Carboniferous Limestone and are believed to overstep onto older rocks in the north-west near Chislet.

The Coal Measures comprise mudstones, siltstones and sandstones, with seatearths which are generally succeeded by coal seams. They were laid down in an intermittently subsiding basin in which periods of subsidence were followed by intervals of rest when the basin became filled with sediment, culminating in the formation of coal swamps. Renewed subsidence led to the drowning of the swamp and the decaying vegetation, later to be converted to coal, was covered by more sediment. At rare intervals, often coinciding with the close of a period of coal formation, the basin was inundated by the sea and thin, but widespread, marine beds were deposited. These beds are of value in correlating rock sequences within the coalfield and in effecting broad correlations with other coalfields. However, in this coalfield, their infrequency limits their value and for detailed stratigraphy non-marine lamellibranch faunas and fossil floras are used; nevertheless, the Tilmanstone marine beds played a significant part in establishing the division of the Kent Coal Measures.

The Coal Measures succession in Kent is divided into two major lithological groups, a lower Shale Division and an upper Sandstone Division, which together represent parts of the Lower, Middle and Upper Coal Measures (Fig. 1).

The 700 ft of mudstones with subordinate sandstones of the Shale Division include eight main coal seams and at least four marine horizons. Non-marine shells indicating the Zone of *Carbonicola communis* occur between the Kent No. 14 and No. 13 Seams, but no evidence has been found of the presence of the underlying *Anthraconaia lenisulcata* Zone or of the *Gastrioceras subcrenatum* Marine Band which elsewhere defines the base of the Coal Measures. The Ripple Marine Band, which is found locally up to 30 ft above the Kent

No. 12 Seam, is the equivalent of the Clay Cross Marine Band of Yorkshire and the Amman Marine Band of South Wales which mark the junction of the Lower and Middle Coal Measures. The beds between the Ripple and the Lower Tilmanstone Marine Bands belong to the Upper *Anthraconaia modiolaris* Zone and the Lower *Anthracosia similis–Anthraconaia pulchra* Zone. The Lower Tilmanstone Marine Band occurs in the highest part of the Shale Division, about 120 ft to 160 ft above the Kent No. 7 Seam. This is now widely recognized in the coalfield but it has not been possible to correlate it with marine bands in other coalfields; it is probably equivalent to the Mansfield Marine Band of Yorkshire and the Cefn Coed Marine Band of South Wales. Another marine horizon, the Upper Tilmanstone Marine Band, has been recorded some 50 ft higher in the succession at Tilmanstone.

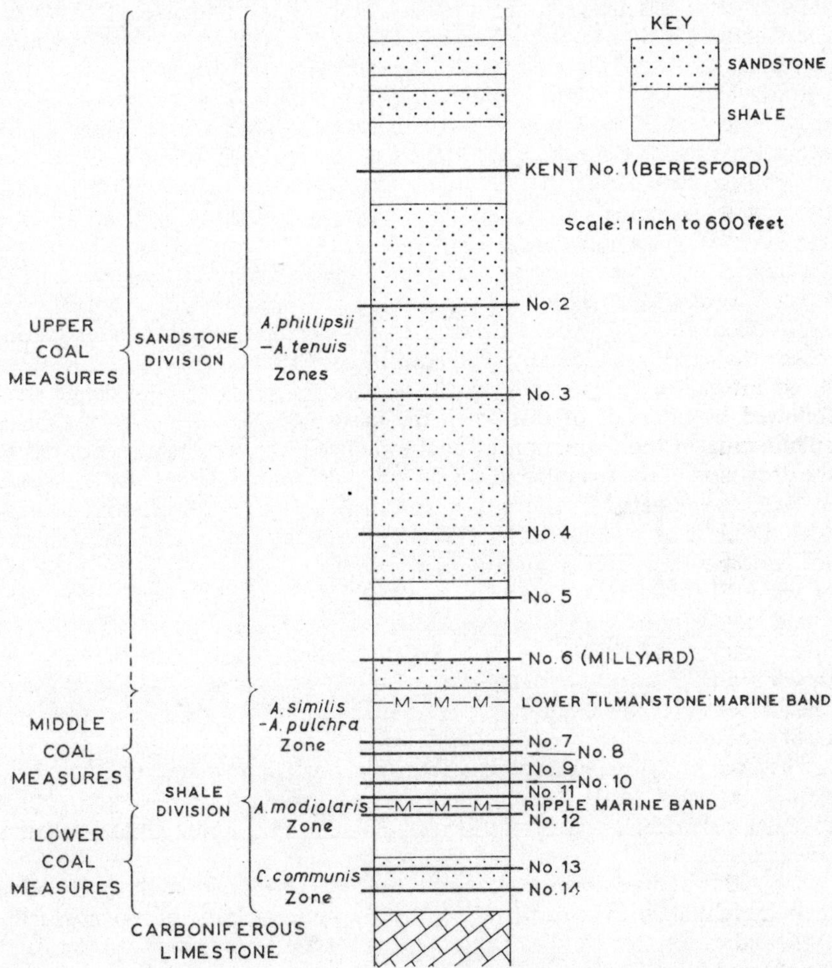


FIG. 1. *Generalized section of the Coal Measures of Kent illustrating the probable zonal classification*

(Based on Stubblefield, C. J., *in* Trueman, A. E. 1954. *The Coalfields of Britain.* London, and others.)

The Sandstone Division is about 2200 ft thick and consists of sandstones and sandy shales with six main coal seams. Its base is taken at the bottom of a 100-ft sandstone group occurring beneath the Kent No. 6 Seam and represents in part the combined zones of *Anthraconauta phillipsii* and *Anthraconauta tenuis*.

The non-marine faunal evidence, although not entirely conclusive, indicates a hiatus between Middle and Upper Coal Measures representing the upper part of the Upper *A. similis–A. pulchra* Zone and part of the *A. phillipsii* Zone; it also supports the correlation of the Lower Tilmanstone Marine Band with the Mansfield Marine Band.

The nature of the coals is discussed in Chapter 9.

# 3. Concealed Strata—Mesozoic Systems (including Jurassic exposed at the surface)

## Triassic System

Throughout most of Permo-Triassic times the Wealden area probably existed as land undergoing sub-aerial denudation in an arid or semi-arid climate. Red marls and breccias, similar to those found in proved Permo-Triassic deposits, have been recorded from boreholes at several localities, for example Brabourne, Henfield, Penshurst and Shalford, directly overlain by Rhaetic or Lias. In the absence of conclusive palaeontological evidence it is not yet possible to state whether these deposits are all of the same age and whether they are late Carboniferous, Permian or Triassic. Some may possibly even be Devonian.

In late Triassic times the transgressive Rhaetic sea invaded the western part of the area which was later to become the axis of the Mesozoic trough. The most complete record of Rhaetic deposits in the Weald is at Shalford, where argillaceous detrital limestones and dark shales containing lamellibranch shell fragments likely to be *Rhaetavicula contorta* were recorded from −5171 ft O.D. to −5225 ft O.D. At Henfield, Dr. W. G. Chaloner has suggested, on plant evidence, a Rhaeto-Liassic age for a series of shales, marls and breccias commencing at −4855 ft O.D.; a similar, but unfossiliferous, sequence occurring at −4458 ft O.D. at Penshurst has been regarded as Rhaetic on lithological grounds.

## Jurassic System

Although the Mesozoic transgression commenced in the Rhaetic, it was in the Lias that it had its most spectacular results in the Wealden District. Such was the rapidity of the incursion and of the formation of the sedimentary trough, that by the end of the Lower Lias the Jurassic sea had almost reached its maximum extent and in the central part of the basin over 800 ft of sediment had accumulated. At that time the northern and eastern margins of the trough lay in the Chatham–Canterbury–Dover area (Fig. 3) and although this shoreline was pushed inland by the later Jurassic transgressions, nevertheless, this area remained as a littoral zone until well into the Cretaceous period. The Lower Lias is overstepped by the Middle and Upper Lias which, in their turn, are overstepped by the Inferior Oolite and the Great Oolite Series, the maximum limits of the Jurassic sea for which we have evidence being in late Great Oolite (Forest Marble) times. It is possible that the Forest Marble was itself overstepped by later transgression of the Oxford Clay, Corallian or Kimmeridge Clay, but during Lower Cretaceous times uplift and erosion of the margins of the basin, as evidenced by the presence of derived Oxford Clay fossils in the Lower Greensand and by Kimmeridge Clay fossils and Portlandian pebbles in the Wealden Series, removed the littoral facies of these deposits. At the present day these Upper Jurassic rocks form a series of arcuate sub-Cretaceous outcrops beneath the Dover–Canterbury–Chatham area in which the younger formations lie progressively nearer the axis of the Mesozoic trough (Fig. 4). Throughout Portlandian times the basin steadily contracted until eventually it became so restricted that the overlying Purbeck Beds were deposited in a predominantly non-marine basin.

Over most of our area the lithology of any given Jurassic formation remains remarkably constant despite great variations in its thickness and in the total thickness of the Jurassic rocks deposited. This implies that these beds were laid down under essentially similar conditions and that the rates of sedimentation and downwarping maintained a delicate equilibrium throughout the period. There is no evidence to suggest that the deposits in the central part of the trough are generally of a more deep-water facies than those nearer the margins, except the deposits which occur very close to the shorelines. The trough subsided continually, though at varying rates, throughout the Jurassic period, there being increases in the rate of subsidence during Lias, Corallian and Kimmeridge Clay times. In Fig. 2, which shows the culmulative thicknesses of the Jurassic at the present day, the isopachytes do not give a complete picture of the basin because some of the Upper Jurassic in the margins of the basin has been removed by Cretaceous erosion. This, however, is not as misleading as it might at first appear since there is reason to believe that the maximum extent of the basin probably was not much greater than that shown in Fig. 2.

As long ago as 1822 W. D. Conybeare and W. Phillips noticed the rhythmic manner in which limestone is frequently followed by clay and clay by sand in the Jurassic sequence. This rhythm occurs several times over and probably reflects changes in the surrounding land area and in the climate affecting it rather than in the depth of water in the basin. During periods of limestone formation conditions of deposition were probably similar to those existing in the central Bahama Banks region, between Florida and Cuba, at the present day. Here calcareous sediments similar to the limestones in the Inferior Oolite, Great Oolite Series, Corallian and Portland Stone, are accumulating in warm, shallow, current-agitated waters free from clastic sediment. Similar conditions in Jurassic times were followed by a change of climate in the nearby land areas from one of aridity to one of humid tropical aspect. This gave rise to large, sluggish rivers flowing over a deeply weathered, heavily afforested landscape. The muds deposited under these conditions now constitute the Lias, Oxford Clay and Kimmeridge Clay, which, despite their fine grade are probably relatively shallow-water deposits. Gradual epeirogenic uplift of the land area caused rejuvenation of the rivers, which in turn carried coarser sediment into the basin, depositing the more sandy parts of the Lias, Inferior Oolite, Great Oolite Series, Corallian, Kellaways Beds and Portland Beds.

The rich fauna and flora of the Jurassic period contains a great variety of species. In the marine deposits two major types of fossil assemblage can be recognized; the clay formations are characterized by ammonites and lamellibranchs, with subordinate numbers of brachiopods, echinoids, crinoids, foraminifera and occasional fish and aquatic reptiles. In the more turbulent environment of the calcareous deposits brachiopods and lamellibranchs predominate over gastropods, corals (which in the Corallian formed important reefs) echinoids and the more robust ammonites. The rapid

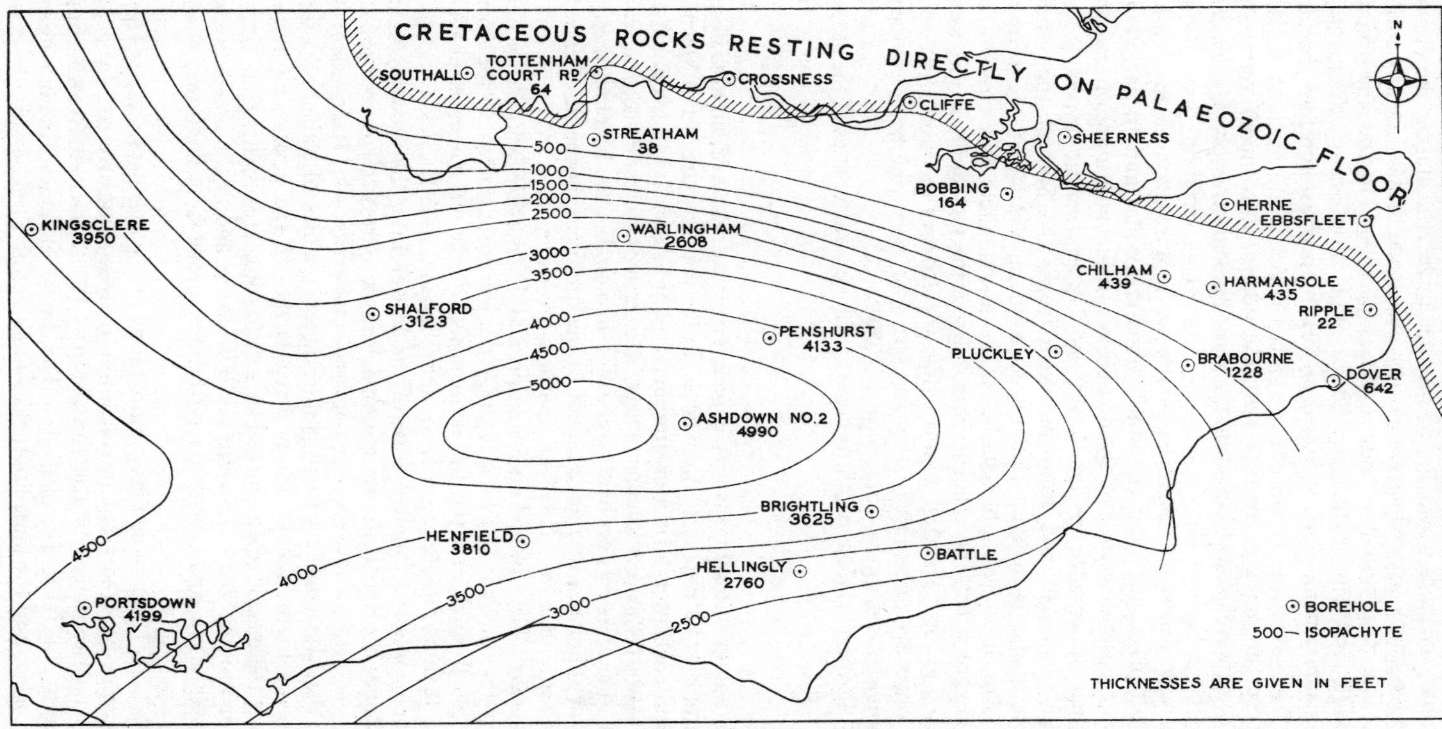


FIG. 2. *Isopachyte map of the Jurassic rocks of south-east England showing the depth of the Jurassic sedimentary basin*

evolutionary changes which the ammonites underwent during the Jurassic, and the frequency with which they occur, has made them eminently suitable for dividing the system up into a series of zones. In the limestones of the Middle and Upper Jurassic, where ammonites occur infrequently, a complementary zonal-scheme, based on brachiopod assemblages, has been used.

On land the dinosaur reptiles were the dominant group of vertebrates: many forms were present including the giant bipedal carnivore *Megalosaurus* and the large herbivorous *Cetiosaurus*. As far as vertebrate habitation of the sea was concerned, there were aquatic reptiles such as the ichthyosaurs and plesiosaurs and the amphibious crocodiles and turtles. Flying reptiles, the pterodactyls, and the first birds, *Archaeopteryx* and *Archaeornis*, made their appearance in the Lower and Upper Jurassic respectively. A few small mammals and some primitive frogs, the first of the modern amphibians, also occurred. The Jurassic landscape carried a vigorous and diverse plant life. Ferns, horsetails, cycads, and conifers were common and the ginkos, of which the sole survivor today is the maiden-hair tree, were a flourishing group. The first angiosperms, ancestors of the modern flowering plants, probably appeared in the Jurassic, but they did not become an important element in the flora until the Cretaceous.

The following brief descriptions give the chief characteristics of the Jurassic strata of the Weald.

## Lias

The lithology of the Lias is very constant over the whole of our area despite considerable variations in its thickness. In the deepest part of the Mesozoic trough (Fig. 2) the Lias is a maximum of 1250 ft thick but thins north and north-eastwards to a shoreline where it oversteps on to Palaeozoic rocks (Fig. 3). The Lias was probably deposited in a shallow continental shelf-sea which was supplied with fine sediment by mature rivers incapable of carrying coarse clastic material. Three subdivisions are recognized.

*Lower Lias.* The Lower Lias is comprised of grey shales with subordinate thin limestones. Near Crowborough (Ashdown Borehole No. 2) the formation is 840 ft thick and the full sequence of ammonite zones is probably present. It thins rapidly towards the shoreline and is 3½ ft thick at Harmansole, where only the topmost zone of the Lower Lias, the *Prodactylioceras davoei* Zone, is present, the lower zones being progressively overstepped by the higher ones as the shoreline moved eastwards. At Harmansole the base of the Lias contains small well-rounded pebbles of Palaeozoic rocks and appears to be infilling minor irregularities in the underlying surface. Elsewhere the base is often marked by a sandy sphaerosideritic bed. Species of the ammonites *Androgynoceras* and *Oistoceras* and of the lamellibranchs *Astarte*, *Nuculana*, and *Oxytoma* have been recorded from the Lower Lias of Kent.

*Middle Lias.* The Middle Lias is more sandy than either the Lower or Upper Lias and can be subdivided into a lower shaly portion overlain by a pronounced limestone facies. The formation is 125 ft thick at Crowborough, thinning to 14 ft at Harmansole. The fauna includes the brachiopod *Tetrarhynchia*, and the lamellibranchs *Modiolus* and *Protocardia*.

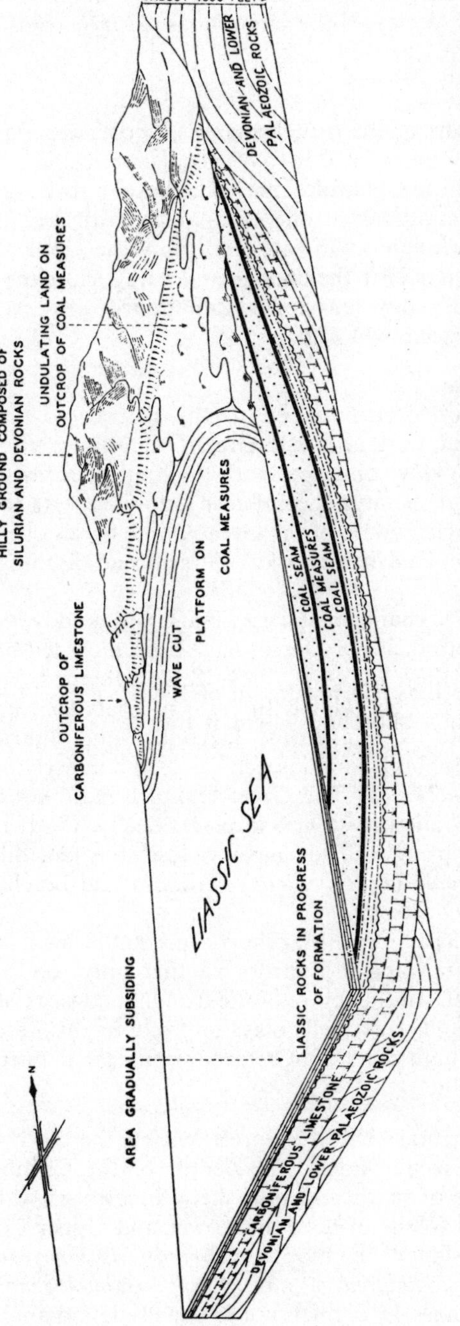


FIG. 3. *Block diagram illustrating the transgression of the Lias sea across the folded Palaeozoic rocks of the east Kent area*

*Upper Lias.* The shales and mudstones of the Upper Lias are overstepped by the Inferior Oolite and the topmost part of the sequence is probably missing. At Crowborough the formation is 287 ft thick, thinning to 9 ft at Dover, where it contains species of the ammonites *Dactylioceras*, *Harpoceras* and *Hildoceras*.

**Inferior Oolite**

In the central part of the trough there is a complete sequence of Inferior Oolite rocks, consisting of 300 ft to 400 ft of oolitic and pisolitic limestones similar to those of the Cotswold area. The basal part comprises as much as 70 ft of oolitic haematitic ironstone, comparable with the Northampton Sand Ironstone of the Midlands. In east Kent only the Upper Inferior Oolite is present; at Dover it is 27 ft thick and is evidently a shoreline facies, consisting of sandstones and sandy limestones with poorly preserved species of the lamellibranchs *Trigonia* and *Lima*.

**Great Oolite Series**

The transgression of the sea on to the Palaeozoic landmass probably attained its maximum extent in late Great Oolite times, the extreme limit of the series being roughly coincident with the limit of Jurassic rocks shown in Fig. 2. Throughout the area the Inferior Oolite appears to be overstepped, and successively higher zones of the Great Oolite Series overstep one another and come to rest on Palaeozoic rocks. Three broad, lithological subdivisions are recognized.

*Fuller's Earth.* The characteristic grey marls and muddy, detrital limestones of the Fuller's Earth facies of Dorset have been recorded only as far east as Brabourne, where they are 44 ft thick, having thinned from 100 ft in the central part of the trough. North and east of Brabourne a sandy, shoreline facies overlaps onto Carboniferous, Devonian and Silurian rocks and at Harmansole and Bobbing contains pebbles of the underlying strata.

*Great Oolite Limestones.* The Great Oolite Limestones consist of rather featureless, buff, oolitic limestones, in places shelly, 150 ft to 200 ft thick in the centre of the trough. They have yielded the lamellibranchs *Liostrea hebridica* and *Trigonia* (*Frenguelliella*) *clavulosa* and brachiopods including *Kallirhynchia* and *Ornithella*.

*Forest Marble.* The Forest Marble is remarkable for its consistently low thickness in our area and it is probable that only the lower part of the formation is present. In the centre of the trough it consists of 20 ft of muddy, rubbly limestones and dark shelly clays and retains this lithology and thickness almost to the limit of its sub-Cretaceous outcrop in north and east Kent.

**Cornbrash**

Between the Cornbrash and the Forest Marble there is a widespread non-sequence in the Wealden area. The details of the Cornbrash are poorly known; it consists of marls and thin shelly limestones which have yielded most of the typical fossils of both the Lower and Upper Cornbrash. These include the zonal index brachiopods *Cererithyris intermedia*, *Obovothyris obovata*, *Digonella siddingtonensis* and *Microthyridina lagenalis*. In east Kent the formation averages 15 ft thick but is usually less than 5 ft in the centre of the basin.

### Kellaways Beds and Oxford Clay

The Kellaways Beds are lithologically variable and represent a transition between the Cornbrash and the Oxford Clay. They consist of ferruginous sandy shales, siltstones and sandstones which are sharply differentiated from the Oxford Clay both in lithology and faunal content. Species of the lamellibranchs *Gryphaea*, in particular *G. bilobata*, and species of *Meleagrinella*, *Oxytoma* and *Pleuromya* are common throughout the sequence. The thickness of the Kellaways Beds is variable, being 35 ft at Dover, 14 ft at Harmansole and about 40 ft in the central part of the basin.

The Oxford Clay consists of bluish-grey shales and mudstones, the normal southern England facies, except in its topmost part which includes ironshot marls of Corallian lithology but containing Oxford Clay ammonites. Species of the ammonites *Kosmoceras*, *Erymnoceras*, *Quenstedtoceras*, *Creniceras* and *Cardioceras* have shown that all the zones of the Oxford Clay are present. Although no shoreline facies of the Oxford Clay is recognized within our area the deposit thins considerably in both a northerly and an easterly direction. At Henfield it is 525 ft thick, 260 ft at Crowborough, 104 ft at Harmansole and only 88 ft thick at Dover.

### Corallian Beds

The Corallian Beds of the Weald form a very thick sequence which is lithologically variable. It is difficult to compare in detail with the standard Dorset sequence, but the following broad correlation has been made by W. J. Arkell for the east Kent area.

| | | |
|---|---|---|
| Upper Calcareous Grit | up to 165 ft | Bluish grey clay with oolitic rubbly limestones overlying a 'millet-seed' iron carbonate (16 ft) which contains the ammonite *Ringsteadia* (cf. the Westbury Iron Ore of Wiltshire). |
| Glos Oolite Series | | Marls and argillaceous limestone. |
| Osmington Oolite Series 125 ft to 135 ft | | Massive, white, oolitic, coralline limestones (coral rag) with calcareous silt partings. |
| Berkshire Oolite Series (lower part only) | | Limestones and marls containing lamellibranchs and Perisphinctid ammonites typical of the '*Trigonia clavellata*' Beds of Dorset. |
| Lower Calcareous Grit | | Probable non-sequence. |

The very thick coralline limestones recorded in the Kent boreholes, and also at Brightling (c. 100 ft) and Warlingham (148 ft), may have been deposited as fringing 'reefs' close to the shore. By contrast the very thick deposits of the central part of the trough (480 ft at Crowborough) are throughout much more argillaceous.

### Kimmeridge Clay

The Kimmeridge Clay shows little lithological variation and consists of shales and mudstones with thin muddy limestones. Only in its lower part, where it is more calcareous and sandy, is there any appreciable change. In the central part of the trough, where the Kimmeridge Clay attains a maximum thickness of over 1700 ft, the full sequence of ammonite zones is present.

Species of the ammonites *Rasenia*, *Pararasenia*, *Gravesia*, *Perisphinctes* and *Pavlovia* and the lamellibranchs *Astarte*, *Exogyra*, *Grammatodon*, and *Protocardia* are common. As elsewhere the lowest part of the Kimmeridge Clay is characterized by an abundance of *Liostrea delta* and *Exogyra nana.* The formation thins northwards and eastwards but is eventually cut out by the Cretaceous overstep before any shoreline facies is reached. At Crowborough it is 1660 ft thick, at Warlingham 702 ft, at Brightling 1136 ft and at Henfield 1082 ft.

**Portland Beds**

Between the Kimmeridge Clay and the Portland Beds there is a complete lithological gradation from shales through sandy shales to sandstones and the junction between the two can be determined only by ammonite zoning. The lithology of the Portland Beds in the Wealden District is markedly different from that of the type area of Dorset, making correlation of the subdivisions difficult. In our area the lower part of the series, the Portland Sand, is more argillaceous than elsewhere and the overlying Portland Stone is represented by calcareous and glauconitic sandstones with no lithological equivalents of either the Cherty Series or of the Freestone Series of Dorset. In east Kent boreholes have provided insufficient faunal evidence even to separate the Portland Sand from the Portland Stone with certainty since ammonites are rare and the brachiopod–lamellibranch faunas are restricted to particular facies. At Penshurst the arenaceous beds are 130 ft thick: at Battle, where they are 140 ft thick, the topmost 6 ft is calcareous enough to be termed a sandy limestone and contains numerous casts of the lamellibranchs *Camptonectes lamellosus*, *Laevitrigonia gibbosa* and *Isognomon bouchardi*. At Warlingham, where the Portlands Beds are 134 ft thick, all three ammonite zones are present including the lowest zone, that of *Zaraiskites albani*.

**Purbeck Beds**

The end of the Portlandian Stage was marked by an important change in the geography of southern England. The shrinking basin of Portland Stone times became so restricted that its connexion with the sea was almost severed and the earliest Purbeck deposits were laid down in hyper-saline lagoons in which gypsum was precipitated. The lagoons were then flooded to form a large, brackish-water lake, probably due to a change from an arid to a more pluvial climate, which remained connected to a sea which lay to the south. Several minor marine incursions occurred, but in general the lake retained its form and low salinity in the Lower Cretaceous until the end of Wealden times.

The junction of the Purbeck Beds with the Portland Stone is sharp but shows no signs of erosion or non-sequence. The lowest 50 ft of the Purbeck consists of shales and anhydrite with four important gypsum seams and is overlain by the finely banded shales and mudstones with subordinate thin limestones which make up the bulk of the formation. Many of the limestones are chiefly composed of lamellibranch or gastropod shells and have a similar origin to those found in the Wealden (p. 26).

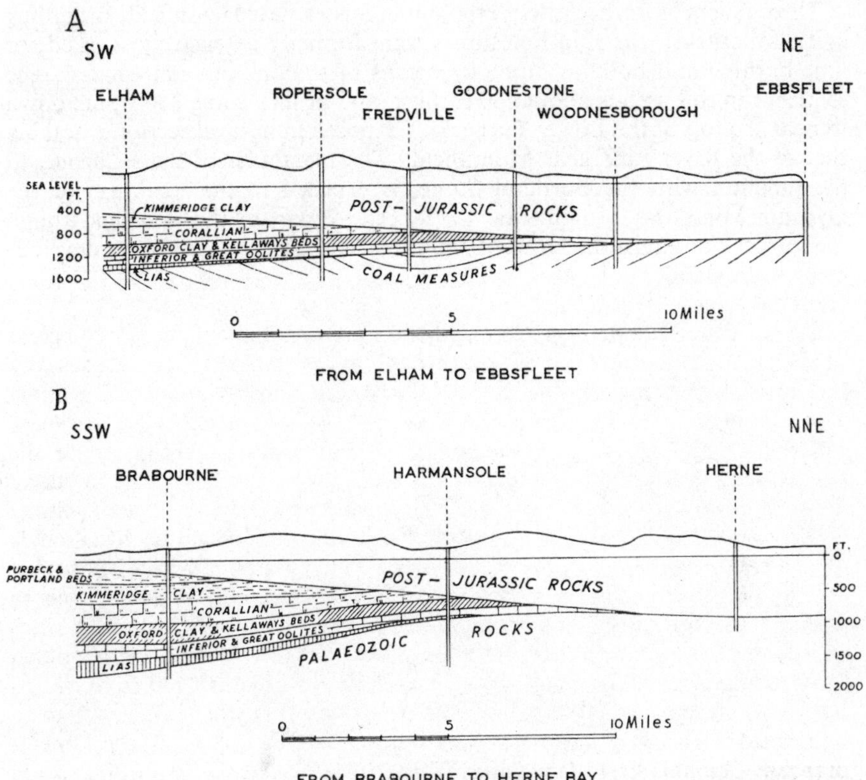


FIG. 4. ***Sections to illustrate the northerly wedging out of concealed Jurassic strata in east Kent***

The Purbeck fauna is varied. There are remains of primitive mammals, many species of reptiles and fish, insects, crustaceans, an echinoderm, lamellibranchs, gastropods and plants.

Though lamellibranchs and gastropods are found in vast numbers at some horizons the number of species represented is small. Ostracods are not only the most abundant fossils but also present the greatest variety of species. Thus the formation has been divided into zones based on ostracod assemblages, mainly composed of species of the genus *Cypridea*. The gypsiferous beds are generally unfossiliferous but throughout the remainder of the sequence the lamellibranchs *Corbula*, *Neomiodon* and *Unio* and the gastropod *Viviparus* are common. The Middle Purbeck contains an oyster bed indicating a widespread near-marine (brachyhaline) incursion–the Cinder Bed of Dorset –which carries its own distinctive fauna. This includes the lamellibranchs *Liostrea distorta*, *Laevitrigonia gibbosa*, *Myrene fittoni* and *Protocardia purbeckensis*, but ammonites, brachiopods and corals are absent, showing that the environment, although more saline, was still not completely marine. F. W. Anderson (1962) has suggested from a study of the distribution of various species of ostracods that other, more-saline periods occurred throughout the series.

Three inliers of Purbeck Beds crop out in Sussex near Heathfield, Brightling and Mountfield; the thin limestones were formerly extensively worked for lime-burning and building stone by means of shallow pits and shafts. The sequence in this area is about 400 ft thick, and of this, some 330 ft, i.e. down to near the top of the Lower Purbeck, is exposed in natural sections, notably that of the River Line near Mountfield. The remainder of the sequence, to the junction with the Portland Stone, is exposed in the workings of the Gypsum Mine near Mountfield. In the central part of the Wealden trough the Purbeck attains a thickness of 560 ft at Penshurst, its maximum development in England.

(A.9690)

View of the Hythe Beds Escarpment from Gibbet Hill, Surrey

(*For full explanation see p. ix.*)

(A.9749)

A. Rusthall Toad Rock, Denny Bottom, near Tunbridge Wells, Kent

B. Hythe Beds at Coombe Quarry, near Maidstone, Kent.

(*For full explanation see p. ix*)

(A.8819)

# 4. Strata Exposed at the Surface—Mesozoic Systems

## Cretaceous System

In the interval between the deposition of the marine Portland Beds and the Lower Greensand (the earliest marine Cretaceous strata), a fresh to brackish-water lake extended over the Weald and into Hampshire, with its northern shoreline running from Croydon through Canterbury towards Deal. Within this lake the lacustrine deposits of the Purbeck were succeeded first by the predominantly deltaic Hastings Beds of the Wealden, the change to coarser sediments being caused by the renewed uplift of the land area which lay to the north, and later by the Weald Clay. Throughout this early part of the Cretaceous period subsidence continued along the Jurassic sedimentary axis, but after the inundation of the Purbeck–Wealden lake by the Lower Greensand transgression this movement became decreasingly important.

From Kimmeridge Clay times onwards sedimentation occurred in two basins, the Speeton basin in north-east England and the southern England basin; which were separated by a ridge of land running through the London area (Fig. 5). In Sandgate Beds (Lower Greensand) times this ridge was breached and a permanent connexion was formed between the two areas. Subsequently the Gault and Chalk transgressions covered the whole of southern England and differential subsidence within the Wealden District effectively ceased, so that during this period a comparatively uniform thickness of sediment was deposited within our area. The close of the Cretaceous was marked by earth-movements which caused folding and erosion with the removal of some of the higher zones of the Chalk.

The junction between the Jurassic and Cretaceous in southern England has long been taken for convenience at the marked lithological change from argillaceous to arenaceous beds which occurs at the base of the Hastings Beds. Elsewhere in Europe, notably in the French Jura and in the Moscow Basin, where the critical part of the sequence is spanned by marine deposits, the junction is defined on ammonite zones. However, a faunal comparison between the marine sequences of the Continent and the non-marine beds of the Wealden District is difficult to effect for there are few diagnostic fossils common to both. Furthermore, the faunas of the Purbeck and Wealden beds evolved in a restricted basin of sedimentation and consequently have more affinity with the earlier Jurassic faunas from which they were derived than with those of the Cretaceous. Dr. R. Casey has recently shown, from a study of the ammonite zones and their inferred equivalents in England, that the base of the marine Cretaceous in northern Europe is everywhere marked by a transgression and that in southern England the Cinder Bed in the Middle Purbeck may represent this transgression. He has suggested therefore, that this latter horizon marks the base of the Cretaceous System in our area.

The invertebrate fauna of the Cretaceous is essentially similar in character to that of the Jurassic. Evolutionary changes were rapid, particularly among the ammonites which in many groups developed aberrant, uncoiled forms. Reptiles continued to be the most important vertebrates. On land the carnivorous dinosaurs reached their maximum size and, in response to this, the herbivores became more heavily armoured and achieved their most bizarre forms. The flying reptiles, the pterosaurs, were by this time less important than the birds which had evolved forms close to those of the present day. Small placental mammals were also present, but were very rare.

The Cretaceous was a critical period in the history of the plant kingdom: from Lower Greensand times onwards the angiosperms (the flowering plants which dominate modern floras) became, for the first time, an important part of the flora. Conifers, cycads and ferns made up the remainder.

The end of the period was marked by the reduction or extinction of several groups of animals, corresponding with world-wide changes in the composition of the planktonic foraminiferal faunas. Among the invertebrates the ammonites and belemnites died out completely whilst the brachiopods were much reduced. Simultaneously the dinosaurs, plesiosaurs and pterosaurs (the ' ruling reptiles ') became extinct.

With the exception of the highest zones of the Chalk and of minor non-sequences throughout the succession, a full sequence of Cretaceous rocks is exposed in the Wealden District.

**Wealden Series**

The Wealden Series consists of lacustrine and deltaic deposits laid down in the northern end of an elongate, subsiding basin, the Anglo-Paris Basin, which ran southwards and was connected to the sea in central France.

The materials which now comprise the Wealden have been derived from earlier Palaeozoic and Mesozoic sediments and at certain horizons characteristic pebbles derived from the older sediments, occasionally containing recognizable fossils, can be identified. From a study of these pebbles and of the distribution of heavy mineral assemblages at selected horizons Professor P. Allen has been able to reconstruct a detailed picture of the geology and geography of the period (Fig. 5). Two large rivers, running from the north and the north-east, supplied sediment to a composite delta which extended southwards into the Wealden Lake, whilst lesser amounts of material, derived from south-west England, were brought into the western part of the lake by a third river. Prominent among the recognizable pebbles are phosphatic nodules from the Kimmeridge Clay and the Portland Beds, Carboniferous cherts and Old Red Sandstone lavas.

Allen has also drawn attention to the striking way in which details of the Wealden succession are rhythmically repeated, in response to a series of rapid minor transgressions and slower regressions which were probably caused either by eustatic changes in sea-level or by climatic changes. The base of a typical rhythm, or cyclothem, is marked by a transgressive pebble bed overlain by dark lacustrine shales which are commonly red stained in their uppermost part. These shales are overlain by the deposits of the outer apron of the delta complex, consisting of interbedded siltstones and fine sandstones, which are in turn capped by the massive cross-bedded sandstones of the main delta front. A further transgression then drowned the delta and lacustrine sedimentation was renewed. Cyclothems occur both on a major scale involving the formations outlined below and on a smaller scale within the formations themselves. A delicate equilibrium was maintained between the rates of subsidence and of sedimentation throughout the period for there is abundant evidence that the Wealden Lake remained continually very shallow.

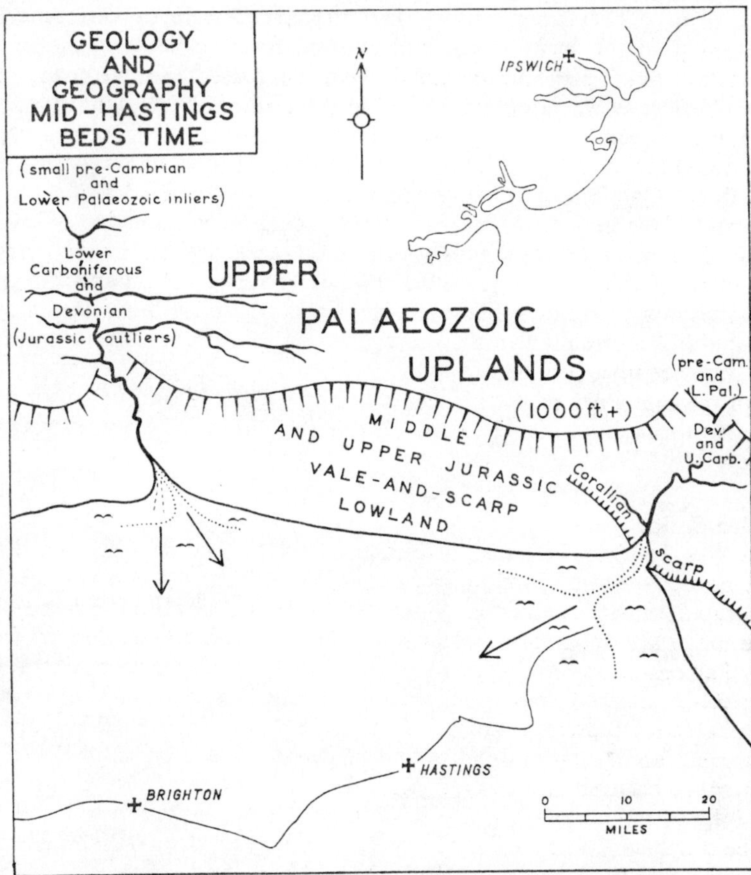


FIG. 5. *The geology and geography of south-east England in mid-Hastings Bed times* (From Allen, P. 1954, *Geol. Mag.*, **91**, with emendations by Professor Allen, 1963)

In the central part of the Weald the Wealden rocks were probably originally over 2500 ft thick, thinning northwards and eastwards and, at the same time, becoming more arenaceous so that the subdivisions described below can no longer be recognized.

The indigenous fauna of the Wealden Lake consists almost exclusively of lamellibranchs, gastropods and ostracods; fish and marine reptiles also occur, but are rare. Material derived from the nearby land areas is relatively common, in particular plant fragments and the remains of reptilian vertebrates. A reconstruction of the landscape on the shores of the lake is shown in Plate IV in which the dinosaur *Iguanodon* and a number of conifers, cycads, ferns and the horsetail *Equisetites* are depicted.

The Wealden Series is subdivided lithologically into six formations as shown below:.

| | | *Formation* | *Thickness* |
|---|---|---|---|
| | | Weald Clay | 400 ft to 1500 ft |
| Hastings Beds | Tunbridge Wells Sand | Upper Tunbridge Wells Sand | 100 ft to 250 ft |
| | | Grinstead Clay | 0 ft to 70 ft |
| | | Lower Tunbridge Wells Sand | 50 ft to 150 ft |
| | | Wadhurst Clay | 100 ft to 230 ft |
| | | Ashdown Sand, including Fairlight Clays | 500 ft to 700 ft |

The Fairlight Clays, Wadhurst Clay, Grinstead Clay and Weald Clay resemble the Purbeck Beds in that they are lake clays deposited in front of the delta (pro-delta deposits). The sands and silts of the Ashdown Sand and the Tunbridge Wells Sand are the actual deposits of successive deltas which grew into the Wealden lake.

### *Ashdown Sand*

The junction of the Ashdown Sand with the underlying Purbeck Beds is conformable and, in east Sussex, is marked by a lithological change from shales to sandstones and siltstones. Elsewhere a similar junction is known in boreholes.

The Ashdown Sand consists of fine-grained, silty sandstones and siltstones with subordinate amounts of shale and mudstone. Within the area of its outcrop the formation shows a regular lithological variation and exhibits, on a reduced scale, the rhythmic deposition characteristic of the whole Wealden succession. In south-east Sussex, around Hastings, the argillaceous parts of the cyclothems are well developed and a series of clay seams, the Fairlight Clays, is well exposed in the cliffs at Fairlight Glen. Northwards from Hastings, where the main mass of the delta lay, the Fairlight Clays become steadily thinner and in the Ashdown Forest they are represented only by pebble beds overlain by thin siltstone beds. At Hastings the Fairlight Clays consist of dark grey shales and mudstones which are commonly patchily red-stained and crowded with sphaerosiderite (iron carbonate) pellets.

The sandstones are usually buff coloured and are massive or thickly bedded, cross-bedding being a common feature in the more massive outcrops. Trough cross-bedding occurs both on a large scale (' scoops ') and on a small scale (' festoons '); minor features such as ripple-marks, washouts, pellet conglomerates, sun-cracks, rain-pits and casts of footprints are also present and testify that current-scour and subaerial exposure occurred. Poorly preserved, elongate plant fragments generally have a roughly parallel alignment, again due to current activity. Lignite, formed from drifted wood, occurs in thin, infrequent, lenticular bands throughout the formation, and in the past has been misidentified as coal. From the evidence of lignite an unsuccessful boring for coal was drilled near Bexhill in 1804. Over much of its outcrop the top of the Ashdown Sand is marked by a massive, fine-grained, quartzose sandstone forming a conspicuous feature. At Hastings this sandstone was formerly quarried for glass-sand.

Fossils are rare in the sandstones and silts except for very fragmentary plant remains and poorly preserved moulds of the lamellibranchs *Neomiodon* and *Unio* and species of the ostracod *Cypridea*. In the Hastings area a conspicuous shale bed containing silicified ' false-stems ' of the tree-fern *Tempskya* occurs near the top of the formation. In the Fairlight Clays plants are well preserved and the sections near Hastings have long been famous for their flora. This includes species of the ferns *Cladophlebis*, *Onchyopsis* and *Weichselia*, the cycads *Otozamites*, *Nilssonia* and *Williamsonia* and the conifers *Pinites*, *Sewardia* and *Sphenolepidum*.

The outcrop of the Ashdown Sand is not continuous but consists of two main masses in which it forms the cores of anticlines, the Ashdown Forest and the district between Uckfield and Winchelsea. Inliers occur in minor folds at Cowden, Penshurst and Goudhurst, and along numerous valley floors where the overlying Wadhurst Clay has been eroded. The thickness of the formation cannot be accurately deduced from the surface outcrops as its base is exposed only around Mountfield and Heathfield, but boreholes at Crowborough, Hellingly and Penshurst indicate it to be 600 ft to 700 ft thick.

Good sections occur around Hastings, where the Fairlight Clays reach their maximum development; although showing a more argillaceous facies of the Ashdown Sand than elsewhere, the cliff sections between Hastings and Cliff End are fossiliferous and exhibit all the sedimentary and lithological features observable inland.

*Wadhurst Clay*

The Wadhurst Clay was deposited on the lakeward side of the Ashdown Sand delta and may be, in part, contemporaneous with it, since the lowest shales of the Wadhurst Clay were forming in the south while sandstones were accumulating in the north. A rise in the level of the sea which lay to the south caused the level of the Wealden Lake to rise and the delta to become flooded. This transgression, the Wadhurst transgression, is marked over the whole Wealden area by a thin bed of pebbly sand or of coarse ferruginous sand called the Top Ashdown Pebble Bed. In individual exposures this Pebble Bed can be seen to cut across minor sedimentary structures in the underlying sandstones but the widespread disconformity which must exist at its base is never seen, suggesting that the transgression was rapid and the disconformity is small.

The Wadhurst Clay consists of dark grey shales, mudstones and pale grey silty mudstones with subordinate beds of silt, sandstone, shelly limestone and clay ironstone. The shales are often finely banded due to rhythmic variations in the coarseness of the sediment, which may have been caused by seasonal climatic variations, the coarser layers being deposited when the rivers supplying the sediment were in flood. Thin silt bands, which are commonly calcareous, occur throughout the sequence and are normally less than 3 in thick. These silts were deposited during times of greater current activity and in places scour the underlying shales to form groove and flute casts. Beds of calcareous sandstone, or Tilgate stone, 3 ft or 4 ft in thickness, occur at several well defined horizons in the Wadhurst Clay and were once extensively quarried for building and roadstone, in particular in the Hastings area where they were known locally as ' Hastings Granite.' The sandstones are usually fine grained and commonly show signs of shallow water deposition and subaerial emergence such as sun cracks, rain pits, casts of reptilian footprints and oscillation ripple marks. Near Crowhurst a Tilgate stone is capped by a pebble bed rich in bone material which has yielded many reptilian remains.

Shelly limestones, rarely more than 3 in thick, occur in association with the darkest, most fine-grained shales and are almost entirely composed of shells of the lamellibranch *Neomiodon* [*Cyrena*] cemented together by calcite or occasionally by siderite. They are winnowed accumulations indicating periods of little sedimentation and in places are rich in small phosphatized bone fragments, teeth and fish scales. Similar limestones composed chiefly of shells of the gastropod *Viviparus* [*Paludina*] occur less frequently.

Much of the iron ore which formed the basis of the Wealden Iron industry in east Sussex and Kent (p. 86) was obtained from the Wadhurst Clay in which it occurs both as nodules and in tabular masses. This clay ironstone ore is sideritic (i.e. a carbonate of iron) and weathers to limonite (i.e. an oxide of iron). The most important and consistent ironstone horizon occurs near the base of the formation.

A thin band of red shales, coloured by disseminated haematite, usually marks the top of the Wadhurst Clay: similar colouring is in places present in the shales immediately beneath some of the Tilgate stone beds.

The more brackish water conditions of the Wadhurst Clay environment, as compared with those of the Ashdown Sand, are reflected by the fossils present: plants, except as spores and pollen, are less common and the non-marine lamellibranchs *Neomiodon medius*, *Unio porrectus* and *U. antiquus* and the ostracods *Cypridea aculeata* and *C. bispinosa* are the dominant members of the fauna, but gastropods, foraminifera and hystrichospheres (a kind of microplankton) have also been recorded from some horizons.

Marsh soil beds crowded with rhizomes and rootlets of the horsetail *Equisetites lyelli* in position of growth, occur at two main horizons: one near the base of the formation at Brede, the other near the top at High Brooms, Southborough, supporting the view that in Wadhurst Clay times the Wealden lake was never very deep.

The outcrop of the formation has roughly the shape of a horseshoe with the bend at East Grinstead and Horsted Keynes, the northern line running from East Grinstead through Wadhurst to Rye, and the southern from near Uckfield to Hastings. The continuity of the outcrop, however, is much broken by faults and the clay rarely covers a wide and continuous expanse, partly due to the presence of outliers of the overlying Tunbridge Wells Sand and to the erosion of valleys through the soft shales to the underlying Ashdown Sand.

The formation thickens westwards across the outcrop, being about 100 ft at Rye, 120 ft at Etchingham, 212 ft at Hailsham and 230 ft at Cuckfield; but a southward thinning and local variations are also apparent.

The outcrops of the Wadhurst Clay and the other Wealden clays are characteristically studded with small ponds, the degraded remains of pits which were dug either for ironstone, ' marl ' or building materials (p. 86).

Bell pits, another common feature, were dug for ironstone, the deep conically shaped workings being incompletely infilled with the shale waste when the ironstone seam had been worked out. Few quarries are now open and natural exposures are commonly obscured by landslip: good sections occur in pits at Sharpthorne, Southborough and Tonbridge, and in cliff sections near Hastings and Cooden.

*Tunbridge Wells Sand*

In the western part of the High Weald the Tunbridge Wells Sand is divided into three, an upper and a lower sandy formation separated by the Grinstead Clay, but in the eastern part of the Hastings Beds outcrop it is not possible to make this subdivision.

The fossils of the two sandy formations consist mainly of poorly preserved plants and lamellibranchs and are similar to those of the Ashdown Sand. Similarly, the fauna of the Grinstead Clay closely resembles the Wadhurst Clay fauna, both in overall content and in the species represented.

The western part of the Tunbridge Wells Sand outcrop, like that of the Wadhurst Clay, is horseshoe-shaped, the northern limb passing from Tunbridge Wells, where it is about 250 ft thick, to East Grinstead (400 ft) and Horsham (300 ft). The southern limb runs from Horsham through Cuckfield (300+ ft) to Uckfield (220 ft) and Hellingly (150 ft). In the eastern Weald the outcrop is very broken and the top part of the sequence is everywhere cut out by faulting: a maximum of 250 ft of strata has been proved.

*Lower Tunbridge Wells Sand.* The lower part of this formation consists of interbedded silts and fine silty sandstones which were laid down at the outermost part of the Tunbridge Wells Sand delta as it encroached upon the Wadhurst Clay lake. These beds are overlain by a massive cross-bedded sandstone, referred to as the sandrock facies, which was deposited at the main delta front. The latter is normally a distinctive clean white quartzose sandstone exhibiting peculiar cavernous weathering along certain bedding planes, although it is not calcareous. In the Tunbridge Wells area the sandstone is generally coarse grained and strings and lenses of small pebbles are common within it: to the south-west, very small scattered pebbles are only sporadically present at West Hoathly; at Cuckfield, where they are absent, the sandstone is fine grained, silty and commonly thickly bedded.

Exposures in the lower silts and sandstones are usually poor but the ' sandrock ' forms numerous natural bluffs and small crags (p. 73) and is well exposed around Tunbridge Wells (Plate III A), Groombridge, East Grinstead, West Hoathly, Ardingly and Uckfield. The formation is approximately 150 ft thick at Tunbridge Wells, 100 ft at East Grinstead and 60 ft at Cuckfield.

*Grinstead Clay.* The base of the Grinstead Clay is marked by the Top Lower Tunbridge Wells Pebble Bed, or by a minor erosion surface, and is analogous to the transgressive base of the Wadhurst Clay. Both the lithology and fauna of the formation are closely similar to that of the Wadhurst Clay and only their relationship to the underlying and overlying strata makes it possible to distinguish the two formations in individual sections.

The Grinstead Clay consists of shales, mudstones and silty mudstones with subordinate beds of silt, clay ironstone and shelly limestones, including one composed almost entirely of ostracod shells. Over much of the outcrop a Tilgate stone, up to 20 ft thick, divides the Grinstead Clay into a lower and an upper portion and it was in this stone, at Cuckfield where it was formerly extensively quarried, that Gideon Mantell discovered the first remains of the land dinosaurian reptile *Iguanodon*. At East Grinstead the stone is absent and an *Equisetites* soil bed occurs at approximately the same horizon. As with the Wadhurst Clay the top of the formation is marked by a reddened clay.

The outcrop of the Grinstead Clay is very broken and runs in an arc from Tonbridge, where it is about 40 ft thick, to Uckfield (30 ft) via East Grinstead (70 ft) and Cuckfield (50 ft). Several minor clay seams, in particular around Flimwell, have been recorded in the Tunbridge Wells Sand of the eastern part of the High Weald, but it has not been possible to correlate any of these with the Grinstead Clay. Artificial exposures of the Grinstead Clay occur at West Hoathly, Dane Hill and Haywards Heath.

*Upper Tunbridge Wells Sand.* The Upper Tunbridge Wells Sand is lithologically similar to the lower part of the Lower Tunbridge Wells Sand and consists of variegated soft mudstones, silts, thinly bedded sandstones and occasional clay ironstones. No distinctive horizons are known within the formation and all the lithologies present are characteristically lenticular and impersistent. The clays commonly weather to red and the silts to mottled grey and orange (' catsbrain '); the junction of the formation with the overlying Weald Clay is gradational and poorly defined.

The Upper Tunbridge Wells Sand is rarely exposed but there are sections at Crawley Down and at Dane Hill where one of the more argillaceous horizons is worked for brickmaking. The formation is about 250 ft thick at Three Bridges and 150 ft to 200 ft at Horsham.

### *Weald Clay*

The Weald Clay was probably deposited at a time when the uplands of the London area had been worn down and the rivers of the source area had reached a mature state. The formation is lithologically similar to the other Wealden clays and consists of shales and mudstones with subordinate siltstones, sandstones, shelly limestones and clay ironstones. When fresh the beds are normally dark grey in colour but weather to mottled yellow and brown. Conspicuous bands of red clay occur at certain horizons, usually in close association with beds of sandstone.

The subordinate beds within the Weald Clay are similar to those described for the Wadhurst Clay. In the shelly limestones the predominance of '*Cyrena*' over *Viviparus* is reversed and limestones composed of the former are rare. In 1875 W. Topley suggested that a sequence of seven sandstones and limestones could be recognized throughout the outcrop of the Weald Clay and this sequence has been confirmed and enlarged upon by more recent work. The most important sandstone, the Horsham Stone, is a thinly bedded, ripple-marked, calcareous sandstone occurring in the lower part of the formation. It is particularly well developed around Horsham, where it is up to 30 ft thick, and was formerly extensively worked in that area for use as paving stones and roofing slates. Two varieties of gastropod shelly limestone occur: the first, Small-'*Paludina*' limestone, occurs in the lower part of the formation and is composed of a small species of *Viviparus*, *V. elongatus*. The second, Large-'*Paludina*' limestone, is known locally by various names such as Bethersden Marble, Laughton Stone, Petworth Marble or Sussex Marble because of its use as an ornamental building stone. It occurs in beds up to 1 ft thick in the middle part of the Weald Clay and is composed of *V. sussexiensis*, a larger species.

Cyclic sedimentation occurs in the Weald Clay of the Maidstone area. The thin sandstone beds in the Weald Clay have a sharply defined base and pass upwards first into red and grey mottled silty mudstones and then through a great thickness of grey mudstones into blue-grey shales with interbedded shelly limestones. These last named are in turn overlain by the basal sandstone of the next cycle. Three major cycles have been recognized, the first is characterized by the Small-'*Paludina*' limestone and the second by the Large-'*Paludina*' limestone. The third is incomplete, the topmost part not being deposited before the area was engulfed by the Lower Greensand transgression. Smaller cycles can also be recognized in varying stages of completeness within the major cycles.

The overall content of the Weald Clay fauna is similar to that of the other Wealden clays. Species of *Viviparus*, the lamellibranch *Filosina gregaria*, of which the '*Cyrena*' limestones are composed, and the ostracods *Cypridea dorsispinata*, *C. tuberculata*, *C. clavata* and *C. valdensis* are the dominant members. Towards the end of Weald Clay times conditions became progressively more saline, heralding the Lower Greensand marine transgression, and the topmost part of the formation contains a fauna reminiscent of the Purbeck Cinder Bed. It includes species of the lamellibranchs *Corbula*, *Nemocardium* and *Ostrea*, the gastropod *Paraglauconia strombiformis*, foraminifera and echinoid spines.

The Weald Clay forms an extensive area of low-lying ground surrounding the outcrop of the Hastings Beds. West of Horsham the Weald Clay outcrop is particularly wide, caused partly by an increase in the thickness of the formation and partly by the low dips near the axis of the Wealden uplift. Away from the main outcrop, small inliers of Weald Clay occur in the Lower Greensand outcrop near Guildford, Dorking, and Maidstone. The thickness of the formation varies considerably, but tends to increase westwards, being 400 ft near Hythe, 800 ft south of Maidstone, 1500 ft near Guildford and 600 ft at Eastbourne.

Natural exposures in Weald Clay are rare, but the formation can be seen in several large pits where it is worked for brickmaking; notable examples occur at Pluckley, Lingfield, Dorking, Warnham, Southwater, Wivelsfield and Berwick, several of which contain sections through sandstones.

### Lower Greensand

Towards the end of Weald Clay times the salinity of the Wealden lake increased as the connexion with the sea grew stronger. Finally the barrier which had existed intermittently between them since Portlandian times was breached and the lake became a shallow, marine bay in which the Lower Greensand was deposited. In the Wealden District the earliest Lower Greensand deposits are lithologically similar to the Weald Clay, but uplift of the land areas caused silts and sands to be deposited in the bay. Further transgressions occurred during Lower Greensand times and the top of the formation is itself overstepped by the Gault. The Lower Greensand was laid down in a variety of shallow-water, near-shore environments. As its name implies, the formation is predominantly arenaceous, but important subsidiary amounts of silty and argillaceous material are present. Chert, ironstone and calcareous deposits also occur in small amounts. When fresh the rocks commonly have a greenish colouration due to the presence of glauconite, but on exposure to the atmosphere this is rapidly oxidized to limonite which gives rise to yellow or reddish brown staining. In the arenaceous parts of the formation there is abundant evidence of deposition in current-agitated waters.

The base is marked by a change from non-marine conditions which is reflected in the fauna. In our area the junction with the subjacent Weald Clay is always sharp and although the Weald Clay was gently folded and eroded locally prior to the deposition of the Lower Greensand, the disconformity between the two is small. The junction with the overlying Gault is marked by a diachronous series of phosphatic nodule beds which overstep the Lower Greensand.

The name Greensand was probably introduced by William Smith to describe the glauconitic sands lying between the Gault and the Chalk in the west of England. Subsequently the name was mistakenly applied to similar deposits in the Weald and the Isle of Wight lying between the Wealden and the Gault, and by the time it was realized that there were two distinct ' Greensand ' deposits, the name was too firmly established to be changed. Consequently, as a compromise the terms Lower and Upper Greensand were introduced.

The Lower Greensand is divided into four major lithological divisions and nine ammonite zones. By using these zones Dr. R. Casey has been able to demonstrate the diachronous nature of the formations shown below; the thicknesses are not to scale.

<table>
<tr><th>Stages</th><th>East Kent</th><th>Surrey</th><th>Sussex</th></tr>
<tr><td>Lower Albian</td><td>Nodule Beds at junction with Gault</td><td>Nodule Beds at junction with Gault</td><td>Nodule Beds at junction with Gault</td></tr>
<tr><td rowspan="3">Upper Aptian</td><td>Folkestone Beds</td><td>Folkestone Beds</td><td>Folkestone Beds</td></tr>
<tr><td>Sandgate Beds</td><td>Sandgate Beds</td><td>Sandgate Beds</td></tr>
<tr><td>Basal Nodule Beds</td><td rowspan="2">Hythe Beds</td><td rowspan="2">Hythe Beds</td></tr>
<tr><td rowspan="3">Lower Aptian</td><td>Hythe Beds</td></tr>
<tr><td>Atherfield Clay</td><td rowspan="2">Atherfield Clay with Perna Bed</td><td rowspan="2">Atherfield Clay</td></tr>
<tr><td>Non-sequence</td></tr>
</table>

The Atherfield Clay and the Sandgate Beds are more fossiliferous than the sands of the Hythe Beds and the Folkestone Beds, which are a poor medium for fossil preservation. Both the latter formations, however, contain phosphatic and ferruginous nodules and beds of sandy limestone which yield a rich fauna. The fauna of the Lower Greensand of the Wealden area is mainly molluscan of a neritic or littoral facies. Lamellibranchs predominate, though brachiopods or cephalopods may be locally abundant; and sponges, polyzoa, echinoids, and gastropods are scattered throughout. Evidence of the proximity of the land area which lay to the north and east, is provided by remains of plants and bones of terrestrial vertebrates.

The outcrop of the Lower Greensand extends in an elliptical belt around the central outcrop of Wealden rocks from Folkestone through Ashford, Maidstone, Sevenoaks, Dorking, Farnham and Petersfield to Eastbourne. Variations in the thickness and lithology along the outcrop are shown in Fig. 6; boreholes in east Kent have shown that the formation dies out along a line running from Pegwell Bay towards Chatham.

*Atherfield Clay*

The Atherfield Clay consists of shales and mudstones which weather to grey, blue, green and brown mottled clays and silty clays. Concretions of clay ironstone and impersistent beds of fine-grained sandstone occur in the lower part of the formation, particularly along the northern part of the outcrop near Maidstone. The junction with the underlying Weald Clay is usually sharply defined, but that with the Hythe Beds is less distinct, the topmost part of the Atherfield Clay commonly being sandy and glauconitic. In Surrey and west Kent fossiliferous concretionary masses of stone occur near the base of the formation and contain the lamellibranch *Mulletia* [*Perna*] *mulleti;* this has been correlated with the *Perna* Bed of the Isle of Wight. In east Kent this thin bottom bed is absent east of Maidstone.

The Atherfield Clay has a rich fauna which includes the ammonites *Prodeshayesites obsoletus* and *Deshayesites forbesi*, species of the lamellibranchs *Resatrix*, *Fenestricardita*, *Freiastarte*, *Mulletia*, *Aptolinter* and *Nuculana*, the corals *Holocystis elegans* and *Discocyathus orbignyanus*, the echinoid *Toxaster fittoni* and the brachiopod *Sellithyris sella*.

Along the northern and western parts of its outcrop the formation reaches a maximum of 60 ft thick at several localities, the thickness in the intervening areas varying between 20 ft and 60 ft. Along the southern limb of the outcrop the formation thins eastwards and at Berwick a thin seam of phosphatic nodules and rolled fossils is probably an attenuated equivalent of the complete formation. A similar deposit to that of Berwick, only 2 ft thick, occurs at Harmansole in east Kent, and is the limit of the concealed extension of the formation.

The Atherfield Clay crops out along the face of the Hythe Beds escarpment and exposures are scarce, the outcrop being much obscured by landslip and by talus from above.

*Hythe Beds*

The lithology of the Hythe Beds varies considerably within the Wealden District (Fig. 6); in Kent and in Sussex east of the River Arun, they consist of alternating layers generally 6 in to 2 ft thick, of hard, bluish grey sandy limestone (' rag ') and grey, loosely-cemented, calcareous, argillaceous sandstone speckled with glauconite (' hassock '). Along the western part of the outcrop the beds are more arenaceous and consist of greenish grey sandstones with subordinate lenticular beds of chert, the latter probably having been formed by re-precipitation of silica derived from sponge spicules.

Fossils are locally abundant in the ' rag and hassock ' beds but are rare in the non-calcareous sandstones of Surrey and west Sussex. In the ragstone they are preserved as ' solid ' specimens, but in the hassock are usually crushed flat. The fauna of the Hythe Beds is more varied than that of the Atherfield Clay. It includes the ammonite genera *Cheloniceras* and *Tropaeum*, species of the lamellibranchs *Sphaera*, *Resatrix* and *Linotrigonia*, the belemnite *Neohibolites ewaldi*, the nautiloid *Cymatoceras pseudoelegans*, the brachiopods *Sellithyris sella* and *Sulcirhynchia hythensis*, the echinoids *Holaster benstedi* and *Discoidea decorata* and various foraminifera, ostracods and radiolaria. Bones of the dinosaur *Dinodocus* have been found at Hythe and an important specimen of *Iguanodon* together with an assortment of other vertebrate remains and plant fragments has been obtained from Maidstone. The plants are mainly coniferous and include *Pinostrobus* and *Pitoxylon*.

In east Kent the Hythe Beds thin northwards and eastwards and are absent in boreholes situated only two or three miles from the outcrop. The beds thicken westwards from Hythe, where they are 35 ft thick, to Maidstone (100 ft) and Sevenoaks (160 ft), attaining their maximum of 300 ft near Farnham. From here the beds thin southwards to Midhurst (200 ft) and eastwards towards Berwick, where they are silty and indistinguishable from the overlying Sandgate Beds. In the western part of the outcrop the variations in the thickness of the Hythe Beds may be due to minor folding and erosion prior to deposition of the Sandgate Beds. This has been confirmed by Dr. Casey's observation that in this area the Sandgate Beds rest on differing zones of the Hythe Beds and that in east Kent the upper part of the Hythe Beds is absent, being replaced by a phosphatic nodule bed at the base of the Sandgate Beds. The formation is exposed in numerous quarries, road cuttings and small natural outcrops: good exposures occur at Otterpool Quarry, near Hythe; Coombe Quarry (Plate IIIB), near Maidstone; West Malling and Sevenoaks in Kent, and Godstone in Surrey.

### *Sandgate Beds and Bargate Beds*

The Sandgate Beds are more variable, both lithologically and in thickness, than any of the other Lower Greensand formations. In east Kent they consist of green and grey argillaceous sands or sandstones and dark grey glauconitic silty mudstones with a basal phosphatic nodule bed resting disconformably on the Hythe Beds. At Sandgate the formation is about 80 ft thick and thins westwards to Maidstone where it consists of 5 ft to 10 ft of poorly consolidated glauconitic clayey sand overlain by a seam of fuller's earth up to 6 ft thick. In the Sevenoaks district only thin glauconitic sands are present, but between there and Nutfield, near Redhill, the sequence thickens to about 80 ft, consisting of interbedded glauconitic sandstone and sandy limestone with important seams of fuller's earth. West of Dorking the lower beds, called the Bargate Beds, predominate, and are characterized by layers and lenses of pebbly calcareous sandstone. Farther west they are overlain by ferruginous clayey sands and silts which have been termed the Puttenham Beds. Similar beds between Petersfield and Washington comprise the Sandgate Beds at

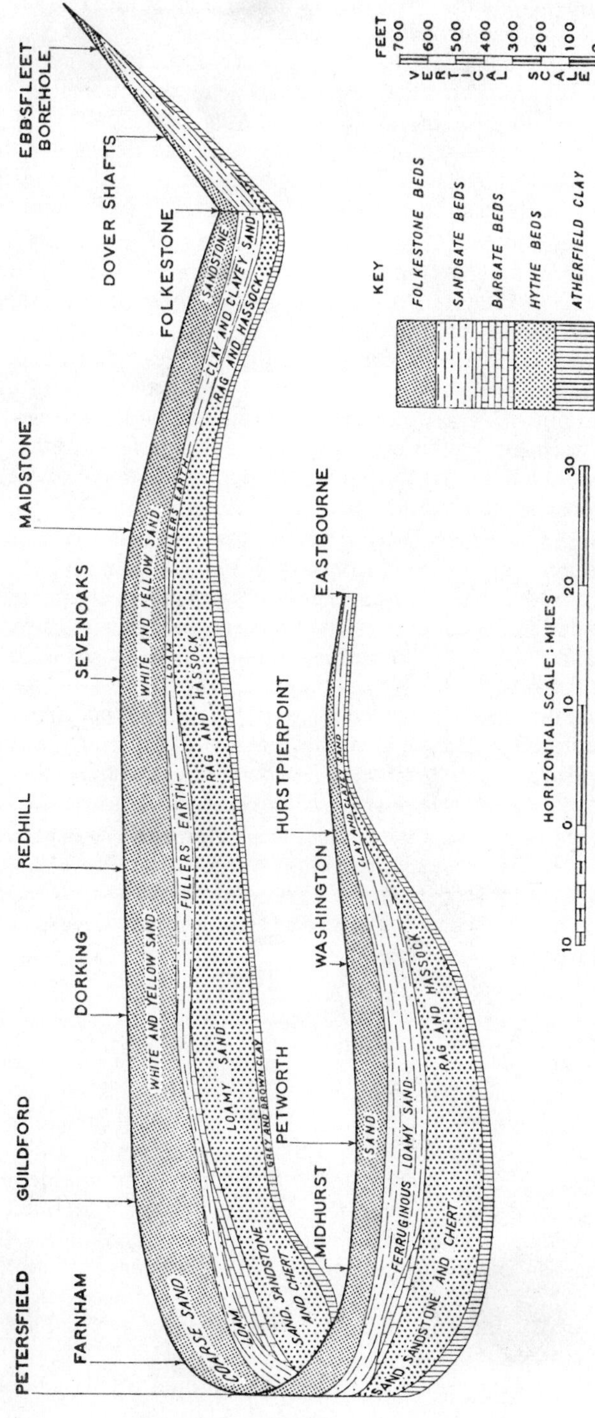


FIG. 6. *Ribbon diagram illustrating the lithological variations of the Lower Greensand in the Wealden District*

their maximum development. They are up to 150 ft thick and include in their upper part a soft, micaceous yellow sandstone, the Pulborough Sand Rock, overlain by dark grey shales known as the Marehill Clay. These two local facies are up to 12 ft and 35 ft thick respectively around Pulborough, between Petworth and Washington. In the Midhurst area Bargate Beds similar to those of west Surrey are also developed below Sandgate Beds which here are disconformable. East of Washington the Sandgate Beds pass into glauconitic silts which thin rapidly eastwards until only 35 ft thick at Eastbourne.

At Sandgate the Sandgate Beds rest on a surface of Hythe Beds bored by the lamellibranch *Myopholas* and at Dover, where the Hythe Beds are overstepped, the top of the Atherfield Clay is similarly bored. At the former locality the basal nodule bed of the Sandgate Beds contains rolled fossils derived from the Hythe Beds. Similarly, phosphatic pebble beds in the Sandgate and Bargate Beds of Surrey contain a high proportion of fish teeth and rolled ammonites. These consist of both indigenous species and of species derived from the Hythe Beds and from Jurassic formations, notably the Oxford Clay, which was, at that time, exposed to the north of the present day Lower Greensand outcrop.

The calcareous and ferruginous parts of the Sandgate Beds sequence contain a rich fauna, but in the glauconitic silts of west Kent and of southern Sussex fossils are rare. The ammonite genus *Parahoplites* characterizes this horizon and species of the lamellibranchs *Chlamys*, *Freiastarte*, *Pseudocardia*, *Pterotrigonia* and *Resatrix*, the brachiopod *Lamellaerhynchia caseyi* [*Rhynchonella sulcata* of authors] are common. The nautiloid *Anglonautilus undulatus*, the echinoid *Toxaster fittoni* and the gastropod *Pleurotomaria anstedi* also occur. The Bargate Beds have a slightly different fauna which includes the corals *Isastrea morrisi* and *Trochosmilia meyeri* and the brachiopod genera *Platythyris*, *Rhombothyris*, *Sellithyris* and *Gemmarcula*.

Good exposures of the Sandgate Beds occur along the coastal section at Sandgate and in the fuller's earth workings around Redhill. Elsewhere the formation is poorly exposed. Quarries in the Bargate Beds near Godalming are now disused but the beds are exposed in the banks of deep sunken lanes in Surrey and Sussex.

### *Folkestone Beds*

The Folkestone Beds consist predominantly of poorly consolidated quartzose sands with seams of pebbles and clay, and veins and doggers of hard ferruginous sandstone (' carstone '). The sands are generally stained yellow to reddish brown by limonite, although clean, white sands (' silver-sands ') also occur. The sands are usually of fine to medium grade, but local variations occur, particularly near the eastern end of the outcrop. At Folkestone the formation consists of coarse yellowish greensands with bands of calcareous and glauconitic sandstone, the whole sequence thinning northwards and eastwards into the concealed Folkestone Beds of the Kent Coalfield. East of Washington, in Sussex, the beds become argillaceous and glauconitic. Other rock types occur locally close below the Gault, particularly around Sevenoaks where a hard green chert –Ightham Stone– and a brown quartzite –Oldbury Stone– are developed at this horizon.

Over much of our area the top of the formation is marked by a series of glauconitic sands and sandy clays containing phosphatic nodule beds, most of which are characterized by the zonal ammonite *Douvilleiceras mammillatum*. In some areas, however, as near Sevenoaks, these beds are lithologically grouped with the Gault. Between Midhurst and Steyning, in Sussex, the junction is marked by a thin ferruginous pebble bed or iron-grit (Fig. 7).

Cross-bedding is well developed in the sands, particularly in the upper part of the formation. In places this feature, coupled with the presence of polished sand grains, occasional dreikanter pebbles and an apparent absence of fossils, gives the deposit a strong resemblance to aeolian dune sands. It is probable, however, that the deposits accumulated in shallow water under the influence of strong currents and that the nearby land area was fringed with sand dunes which were, in part, re-worked and incorporated into the present deposits.

Fossils are rare in the main mass of the sands but the sandstone bands and the phosphatic nodules contain a rich fauna which includes the ammonites *Hypacanthoplites jacobi*, *Leymeriella tardefurcata* and *Douvilleiceras mammillatum*. The first is the zonal index of the highest zone of the Aptian Stage, the others being indices of the two lowest zones of the Albian Stage. Species of the lamellibranchs *Exogyra*, *Lopha*, *Pterotrigonia* and *Oxytoma* occur throughout the sequence. The echinoids *Phyllobrissus* and *Holaster*, the gastropod *Margarites*, annelids, driftwood, fish and reptilian remains also occur.

At Folkestone the formation is 60 ft thick and thickens rapidly westwards to Maidstone (150 ft), Redhill (180 ft) and Farnham, where it attains its maximum of 260 ft. In Sussex the Folkestone Beds again thin eastwards, being 200 ft thick at Petersfield and 100 ft at Washington, but less than 10 ft thick at Eastbourne. The sandy part of the formation is of considerable economic value and numerous large artificial exposures occur at intervals along the outcrop, notably near Folkestone, Redhill, Dorking, Farnham and Washington.

**Gault and Upper Greensand**

Over the whole of southern England the base of the Gault is marked by an important marine transgression, which swept northwards and westwards and pushed back the shoreline of the Lower Greensand sea to the borders of Wales and into northern England. In the Weald proper the Gault rests on the Folkestone Beds, but in north and east Kent it oversteps the Lower Greensand and comes to rest first on Jurassic rocks and then finally on to Coal Measures and Devonian and Silurian rocks in the neighbourhood of the north Kent coast.

The Gault and the Upper Greensand are lithological variants of a single sequence which spans the Middle and Upper Albian, the term Gault being applied to the argillaceous facies and Upper Greensand to the more arenaceous material (Fig. 7). The latter was probably deposited in shallow, current-swept conditions near the shorelines whilst the Gault, also a shallow-water deposit, was laid down in quieter water farther away from the source of the sediment. Although the Upper Greensand is the lateral equivalent of part of the Gault each formation contains a distinctive fauna. That of the

Upper Greensand is dominated by thick-shelled and strongly ribbed, benthonic molluscs which could withstand the strong currents of near-shore environments, whereas the Gault contains a larger proportion of thin shelled benthonic and pelagic forms.

Phosphatic nodule beds occurring within the Gault mark brief halts in deposition (usually referred to as non-sequences), but apart from these minor interruptions a complete sedimentary record of Gault–Upper Greensand times is preserved in the Wealden District.

*Gault*

The Gault consists of dark bluish grey to pale grey soft mudstones and silty mudstones which weather to yellow and brown clays. The basal few feet of the formation are commonly silty or sandy and, at other levels, the clays are generally either glauconitic or calcareous. Phosphatic nodule beds occur at several horizons, notably in the middle of the formation (Fig. 7) where a persistent band of nodules marks the junction of the Lower and Upper Gault. Nodule beds at the junction of the Gault and Lower Greensand were formerly worked in the regions of Folkestone and Farnham for agricultural use.

The Gault contains a rich marine fauna in which molluscs predominate. The formation is divided into four ammonite zones; the zones of *Hoplites dentatus* and *Euhoplites lautus*, which make up the Lower Gault, correspond to the Middle Albian Stage, and the zones of *Mortoniceras inflatum* and *Stoliczkaia dispar* correspond to the Upper Albian (Upper Gault). Other cephalopods which are usually present include the ammonites *Anahoplites planus*, *Dimorphoplites biplicatus* and *Hamites maximus* and the belemnite *Neohibolites minimus*. Lamellibranchs, in particular species of *Inoceramus*, are common and include *I. concentricus*, *I. sulcatus*, *Nucula pectinata*, *Cucullaea glabra* and *Pinna robinaldina*. The gastropods *Gyrodes genti* and *Perissoptera marginata* are characteristic and tubes of the marine worm *Rotularia concava* are also found. In addition to these, brachiopods, echinoids, corals, crustaceans, teeth and bones of fish and drift wood also occur. Washed samples of the clay are usually rich in foraminifera.

Locally the thickness of the formation varies considerably, but there is a general westwards thickening across the outcrop. At Folkestone, and beneath the Chalk of east Kent, it is about 130 ft to 150 ft thick and thickens to 225 ft north of Maidstone, 280 ft at Reigate and, over much of south and west Sussex, to about 300 ft.

The Gault forms a narrow outcrop at the foot of the Chalk escarpment and is in places obscured by downwash. Natural exposures are rare, but good examples occur at Copt Point, Folkestone (Plate IX B), which is the type section of the English Gault, and in a disturbed state in the foreshore beneath the Chalk cliffs at Folkestone Warren and at Eastbourne. Large brickpits at Ford Place, near Wrotham and at Greatness Lane, Sevenoaks in Kent, provide good inland exposures of the Gault.

*Upper Greensand*

The Upper Greensand of the Wealden District shows great lithological variety, in which three broad rock-types can be recognized (Fig. 7). Poorly

Idealized Landscape on the Shores of the Wealden Lake
(*For full explanation see p. ix*)

Ammonites from the Gault and Lower Greensand

1. *Tropaeum drewi* Casey
2. *Parahoplites maximus* Sinzow
3. *Douvilleiceras mammillatum* (Schlotheim)
4. *Euhoplites lautus* (Parkinson)
5. *Mortoniceras inflatum* (J. Sowerby)

(*For full explanation see p. ix*)

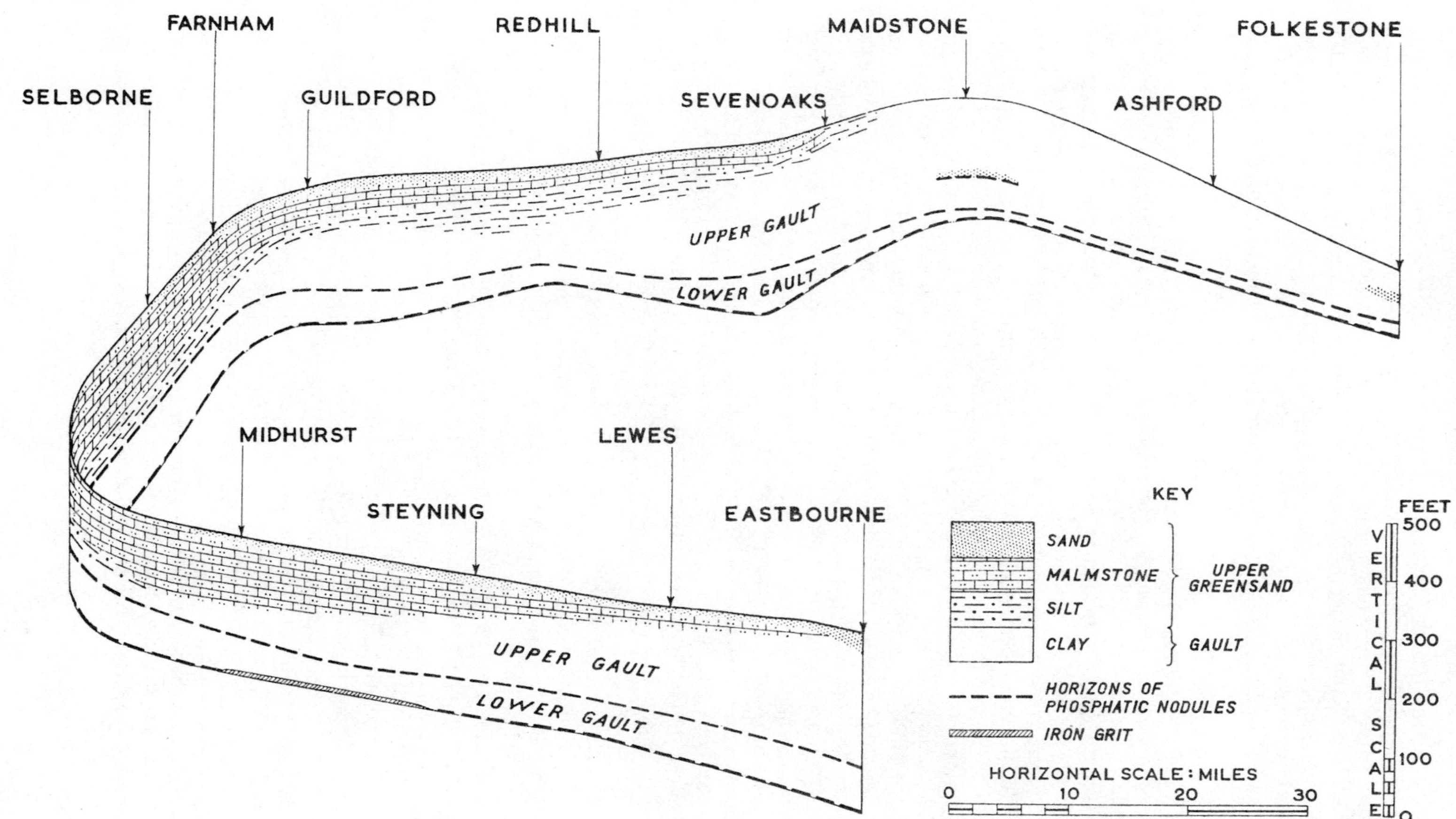


FIG. 7. *Ribbon diagram showing the relationship of the Gault to the Upper Greensand in the Wealden District*

consolidated siltstones usually occupy the lower part of the formation and form a transitional junction with the Gault. The silts are overlain by a predominantly sandy series of beds which includes small amounts of clay and silt. Much of the sandstone is referred to as ' Malmstone ', a pale coloured rock containing abundant sponge spicules and a high proportion of colloidal (soluble) silica with clay, calcareous matter and some mica. Two varieties of Malmstone occur. The first, a hard, compact siliceous sandstone containing small amounts of calcareous cement occurs in beds up to 2 ft thick separated by thin sandy partings. Around Reigate this sandstone was formerly mined for use as building stones and as refractory material for lining furnaces. This latter usage led to the name ' Firestone ' being given to these beds. The second variety, known as ' Hearthstone ', is a soft, friable, greenish grey calcareous sandstone, in places becoming a siliceous limestone, which was formerly used for whitening hearths. The top of the Upper Greensand is usually marked by clayey sandstones speckled with glauconite, which are dark olive green when fresh but they weather to grey and brown.

In our area the Upper Greensand is confined to the Upper Albian and although species of the Hoplitid ammonites occur, the zonal index fossils *Mortoniceras inflatum* and *Stoliczkaia dispar* are rare. Lamellibranchs such as *Chlamys* (*Aequipecten*) *aspera*, *Entolium orbiculare*, *Exogyra conica*, *Grammatodon carinatus* and *Neithea quinquecostata* predominate but the gastropods *Gyrodes genti*, *Torquesia granulata* and occasional sponges such as *Doryderma dichotomum* and *Hallirhora costata* also occur.

The Upper Greensand is thickest in the western part of the Weald, reaching a maximum of nearly 200 ft at Selborne and thinning northwards to 80 ft at Guildford and southwards to 100 ft at Midhurst. In Sussex the formation thins eastwards to about 30 ft at Eastbourne. Natural exposures of the Upper Greensand are rare but small outcrops are seen on the foreshore at Eastbourne and in sunken roadways in the Selborne area. The Firestone and Hearthstone mines near Reigate are now disused and many have collapsed.

**Chalk**

The relatively local downward movement of the land that commenced during Lower Gault times was the precursor of a remarkable subsidence which affected much of Central and Western Europe, including practically the whole of England and Scotland and parts of Wales and Ireland. This encroachment of the sea on land areas is termed the ' Cenomanian transgression,' the name being derived from ' Cenomanum,' the Roman name of the town of Le Mans about 120 miles south-west of Paris, where deposits associated with early stages of the subsidence have been closely studied.

Over the whole of the gradually submerged region a great thickness of white calcareous mud was laid down; this material is now termed ' chalk.' Land nearest to our area was probably on the site of southern Ireland, with the possible exception of some islands formed by the then representatives of the Ardennes. Except at the beginning of Chalk times, little detrital matter brought by rivers into the sea reached our district; this was probably due to the great distance from land, but the climate at that time may have been so hot and dry that land bordering the Chalk sea was desert, and rivers consequently few. Although but little land-derived material is present in chalk, occasional far-travelled pieces of rock occur; these vary from minute fragments to boulders nearly a foot long, and are thought to have been transported by floating masses of seaweed or as gastroliths, ' stomach-stones,' of marine reptiles. Many such pebbles and boulders have been found in the Chalk of the Wealden District, notably from quarries at Betchworth, Surrey, and near Rochester in Kent.

Following the Cenomanian transgression gentle earth movement was continuous throughout Chalk times, causing fluctuations in the depth of the sea but never raising the sea floor above water level.

The Weald proper is surrounded by the Chalk Downs, the North Downs extending from Farnham to Dover and the South Downs from Petersfield to Eastbourne. The greater part of the Chalk downland is occupied by Upper Chalk; Middle Chalk and Lower Chalk crop out chiefly in the scarped slopes of the North and South Downs, and in the bottoms of some valleys; the Lower Chalk crops out at the foot of the escarpments, and is usually marked by extensive areas of arable land, but Middle Chalk is generally confined to the steepest parts of the higher cliff-like slopes.

Chalk is a soft, white, friable limestone, consisting of over 95 per cent of calcium carbonate. It was formerly considered to be made up almost entirely of whole and fragmented microscopic fossils, and thus comparable to the deep-sea foraminiferal oozes forming at the present day on the floor of the Atlantic. In fact the proportion of microscopic animals, chiefly foraminifera, never exceeds 5 to 10 per cent of the rock. Other investigators held the view that chalk might be a chemical precipitate or that bacterial action was involved in its formation. However, recent examination by Mr. M. Black of chalk specimens under the electron microscope has shown that the calcareous particles are calcite of organic origin. Ordinary white chalk consists of a coarse fraction composed of shell debris and foraminifera embedded in a fine matrix of coccoliths (microscopic calcareous bodies produced by planktonic algae) and their disintegration products. Coccoliths are present in vast numbers and in all stages of disintegration down to individual component crystals. The proportion of coarse to fine material varies considerably within certain limits, giving rise to chalks of different lithological character. The presence of a high proportion of *Inoceramus* prisms or other shell debris produces a friable chalk with a rather gritty texture; nodular chalk contains either abundant foraminifera, problematical bodies termed " spheres," or both, while the coccolith fraction predominates in the soft white chalks of the *Micraster* zones. Modern precipitated oozes, such as those forming on the Bahama Banks, are composed almost entirely of minute aragonite crystals with a negligible proportion of coccolith material and relatively little shell debris.

Though at first sight the Chalk has a uniform appearance throughout its thickness, a wide variety of distinct lithologies is present. Three main subdivisions may be further divided by fossils into a number of zones (Fig. 8). Little lateral variation occurs, however, since at any given time conditions were similar over the whole area and the same sequence of beds is recognizable throughout the length of the outcrop. Differences in lithology are thought to reflect changes in the depth of the sea. The Chloritic Marl, laid down at the commencement of the Cenomanian transgression, contains much detrital material owing to the comparative proximity of land, from which rivers brought sand and mud. The bulk of the Chalk, however, was probably laid down in a relatively shallow sea, about 100 fathoms deep, i.e. below the level of wave action. The Melbourn Rock, and other beds of nodular chalk were formed during periods of temporary shallowing of the sea and show signs of penecontemporaneous current action and submarine erosion.

The Upper Chalk in the Wealden District is everywhere characterised by the presence of flint, and in fact was once termed the Chalk with Flints to distinguish it from the underlying divisions. Locally, grey flint is found as small nodules in the Lower Chalk; it is largely absent from the Middle Chalk but occurs in the upper beds of this division. Flint consists of an intimate mixture of soluble and insoluble silica and is found either as nodules, isolated or in layers, or as tabular sheets, usually parallel to the bedding but sometimes occupying vertical or oblique cracks and fault planes. The origin of flint remains controversial. It may have been formed subsequent to the deposition of the chalk as a result of the solution by percolating ground waters of fossils such as sponges which have siliceous skeletons; on the other hand, much appears to be of inorganic origin, precipitated from sea water as a gel, a jelly-like colloidal solution, either contemporaneously with deposition of the chalk or preceding its consolidation.

Heavy rusty brown nodules, which occur particularly in the Lower Chalk, when broken open reveal a radiating mass of brassy crystals of an iron sulphide mineral, either pyrite or marcasite; a twinned variety, 'spear pyrites,' occurs notably in the Chalk Marl between Folkestone and Dover. Marcasite is readily oxidized, tarnishing and decomposing rapidly on exposure to the atmosphere. The nodules have a superficial resemblance to certain types of meteorite or 'thunderbolt,' with which they have sometimes been confused.

Compared with that of the underlying Gault the fauna of the Chalk is characterized by echinoids and brachiopods rather than by ammonites, the latter being abundant only in the lower part of the formation. The fauna is a rich one but in most parts of the Chalk highly fossiliferous bands are comparatively restricted. The Chalk succession is everywhere incomplete in Britain, and in our area a large part of the Upper Chalk is missing. Where these beds can be studied it is seen that the end of Cretaceous times marked a big change in marine faunas, with the extinction both of ammonites and belemnites and also of the giant marine reptiles.

The Chalk gives rise to extensive areas of characteristic undulating downland scenery, dissected by coombes and steep sided dry valleys. It is about 800 ft thick in the north-western part of the Wealden area, increasing to 1200 ft near Chichester.

*Lower Chalk.*

A considerable amount of argillaceous and arenaceous matter is present in the Lower Chalk, the proportion of non-calcareous substances varying from about 50 per cent of the total in the lowest beds to about 10 per cent in the upper. The lowest bed, named the Chloritic Marl, varies from a few inches up to about 10 ft in thickness. It is a sandy glauconitic marl, sometimes with phosphatic nodules and remanié fossils, mainly at the base. The

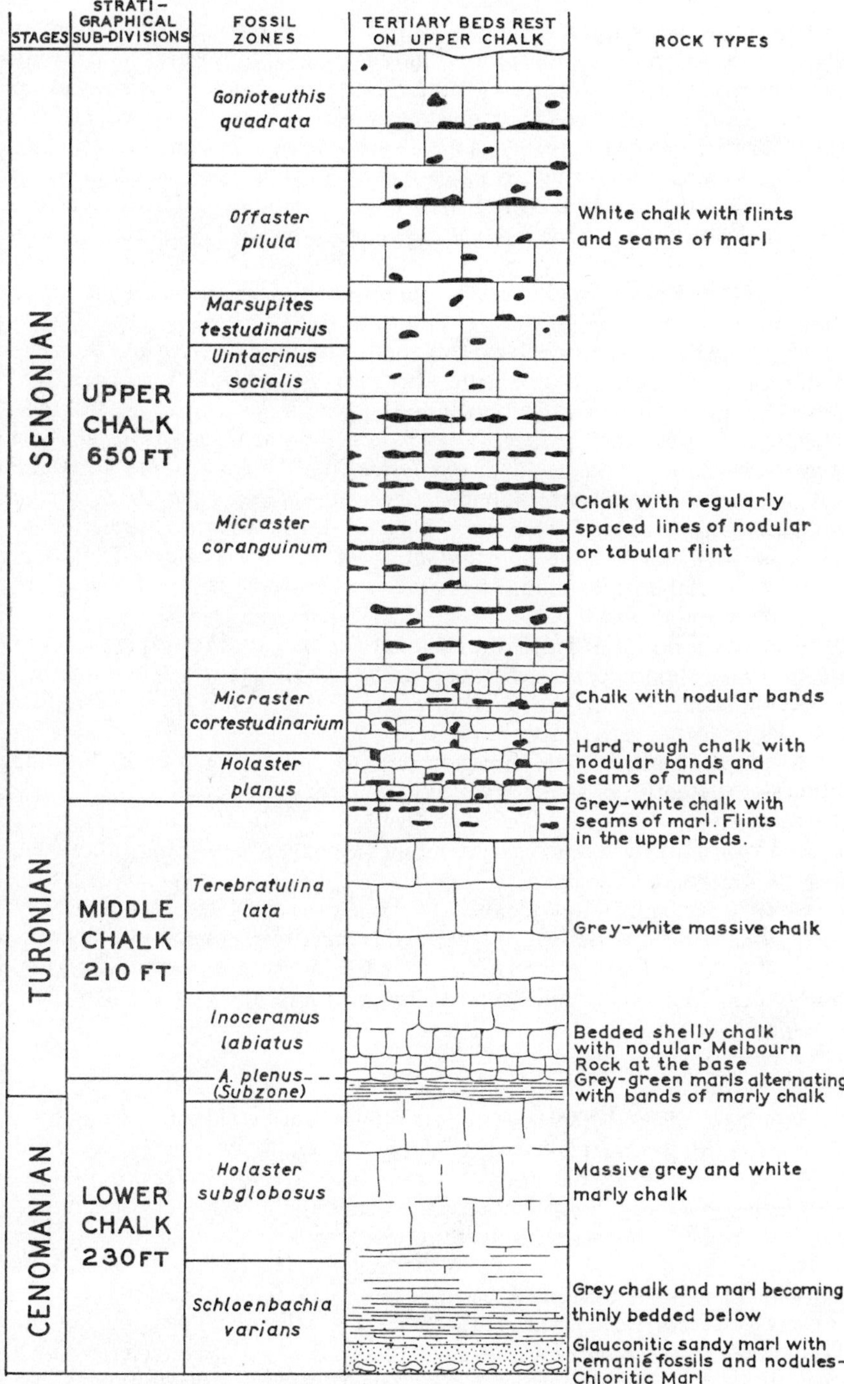


Fig. 8. *Generalized section of the Chalk of the Wealden District showing the zonal classification, lithological divisions and thicknesses*

name owes its origin to the misidentification of the glauconite, which is green when fresh, as chlorite. There is a gradual passage upwards into thinly bedded marly chalk, alternating with harder bands, which in turn passes up insensibly into dull grey chalk diversified with irregular marly partings. These beds are grouped together as the Chalk Marl, but in our area they have no distinct upper limit. They are succeeded by massively bedded chalk which is predominantly grey in the lower part and is frequently referred to as the Grey Chalk. Above this come the *plenus* Marls, a few feet of alternating beds of yellowish or dark greenish grey marls, termed ' soap ' by quarrymen, and lighter coloured marly chalk; in the upper part the belemnite *Actinocamax plenus* is common.

The Lower Chalk is divided into two zones with the thin *A. plenus* Subzone at the top. The lower zone, named after *Schloenbachia varians*, is characterized by other ammonites belonging to the genera *Schloenbachia*, *Mantelliceras*, *Calycoceras* and *Turrilites*, as well as lamellibranchs such as *Aequipecten beaveri*, *Inoceramus crippsi* and *Plagiostoma globosum*. Some beds are crowded with the small brachiopods "*Rhynchonella*" *grasiana*, "*R.*" *martini* and *Orbirhynchia mantelliana*, while siliceous sponges formerly referred to the genus *Plocoscyphia* are common at the base of the zone. The zonal ammonite is rather uncommon, but other species such as *S. subvarians* are useful zonal indicators.

The upper zone, named after the echinoid *Holaster subglobosus* is poorer in fossils. Large ammonites of the genus *Acanthoceras* occur as well as numerous echinoids such as *Discoidea cylindrica* and *Tetragramma* [*Pseudodiadema*] *variolare*.

The *plenus* Marls belong lithologically to the Lower Chalk, but the ammonites (mainly species of *Metoicoceras*) have closer affinities with those of the overlying *Inoceramus labiatus* Zone of the Middle Chalk. For this reason the *plenus* Marls are regarded either as a subzone of the *labiatus* Zone or as an independent zone.

The Lower Chalk is well exposed in the classic coast sections at Beachy Head and Folkestone but can be more conveniently examined in numerous quarries at the foot of the Downs; among the largest are those at Dorking, Betchworth, Merstham and Oxted, in the Medway and Arun valleys, and at Lewes.

*Middle Chalk.*

At the base of the Middle Chalk is a lithological break marked by about 10 ft of hard, marl-streaked, greyish yellow chalk enclosing very hard kernel-like nodules. This nodular chalk (the Melbourn Rock) and the chalk which overlies it has a gritty texture due to the presence of comminuted *Inoceramus* shell; it passes gradually upward into massively bedded, white chalk with thin grey marly seams in the upper part. In the top 30 ft flints and beds of nodular chalk also occur.

Two zones are recognized in the Middle Chalk, the lower having the lamellibranch *Inoceramus labiatus* as its index fossil; it is characterized by a fauna of small echinoids such as *Cardiaster pygmaeus*, *Discoidea dixoni* and *Peroniaster nasutulus*. The large echinoid *Conulus subrotundus* occurs frequently, as does the brachiopod *Orbirhynchia cuvieri*, which was formerly used as the zonal index. Cephalopods are represented by rare examples of the ammonite *Mammites nodosoides* and giant ammonites belonging to the genus *Lewesiceras.*

The higher zone, named after the small brachiopod *Terebratulina lata* carries a generally similar fauna but *O. cuvieri* is absent and *I. labiatus* gives way to *I. lamarcki.* In its upper part the zone contains *Micraster corbovis* and *Holaster* (*Sternotaxis*) *planus*, which foreshadow the echinoid fauna of the Upper Chalk.

Good sections in the Middle Chalk are to be seen in the Dover cliffs and in the same quarries as those which have been mentioned as exposing Lower Chalk.

*Upper Chalk.*

The bulk of the Upper Chalk is composed of the familiar soft white chalk with flints, but in the lower part are many thin beds of hard, rough, nodular chalk which owe their character to deposition in shallow water and subsequent lithification by lime, silica and phosphate. At the base it has proved possible to identify over a wide area a detailed sequence of nodular beds, flint bands and a marl seam, using fossil-evidence as a guide. Much of the lowest hundred feet of the Upper Chalk generally has a rough, lumpy texture.

Seven faunal zones have been established (Fig. 8), but over most of the area the succession is incomplete because of gentle folding and extensive erosion prior to the deposition of the Tertiary Beds, which, broadly speaking, rest on successively higher zones towards the south-west of the area.

The basal nodular chalk (*Holaster planus* Zone) contains moulds of fossils belonging to the fauna named after the uncoiled ammonite *Hyphantoceras reussianum.* This fauna is unusual in that it includes aragonite-shelled molluscs such as ammonites and gastropods which are not generally preserved in other chalk facies; hexactinellid sponges are also abundant. Important members of this fauna are the ammonites *Bostrychoceras woodsi*, *Lewesiceras mantelli*, *Scaphites geinitzi*, *Sciponoceras bohemicum* and *Subprionocyclus neptuni*; the gastropods *Bathrotomaria perspectiva*, *Eutrochus schlueteri* and *Solariella gemmata;* and numerous lamellibranch genera including *Barbatia*, *Cardium*, *Cardita*, *Nucula* and *Trapezium.*

In the three lowest zones the echinoid *Micraster* is abundant. Study of hundreds of individuals collected from different beds of the Chalk of Kent enabled A. W. Rowe to demonstrate progressive evolutionary changes in the genus, by means of which this part of the Chalk can be zoned. Above the *Micraster coranguinum* Zone the index fossils of the two succeeding zones are the free-swimming crinoids *Uintacrinus* and *Marsupites.* These are found more commonly as detached plates rather than as complete cups. Of the remaining two zones in our area, the lower is named after the small echinoid *Offaster pilula*, the higher after the belemnite *Gonioteuthis quadrata.* R. M. Brydone has shown that in the *O. pilula* Zone fossils tend to be concentrated in bands and that the zonal echinoid is abundant only in the upper part. Shape variants of the echinoid *Echinocorys* are of particular value in determining horizons within this zone; *Hagenowia rostrata*, an aberrant form of echinoid, is restricted to a band at the top. Only the lower part of the *G. quadrata* Zone is preserved in our area and in this the index fossil occurs infrequently, a more useful indicator of horizon being the microcrinoid *Saccocoma cretacea*.

The rich variety of the Upper Chalk fauna has provided a number of useful guides to horizon in addition to the evolutionary changes in *Micraster*. These include shape variants of *Echinocorys*, and the calyxes of the fixed crinoid *Bourgueticrinus*. The *M. coranguinum* Zone is particularly rich in regular echinoids such as *Phymosoma koenigi*, *Stereocidaris sceptrifera* and *Tylocidaris clavigera*, while the conical irregular echinoid *Conulus albogalerus* is abundant at the top of the zone. Brachiopods are numerous, especially in the lower zones, but decline in number upwards; Terebratuloids in particular become uncommon above the *M. coranguinum* Zone. The Rhynchonelloid *Cretirhynchia* is characteristic and enters in abundance at the bottom of the *planus* Zone; the Terebratuloid *Gibbithyris* and the Rhynchonelloid *Orbirhynchia* continue through from the Middle Chalk. Apart from the *reussianum* fauna, ammonites are exceptionally rare, although the giant *Parapuzosia leptophylla* occurs in some numbers in the upper part of the *Uintacrinus socialis* Zone in the Isle of Thanet. Belemnites are not seen until the top of the *M. coranguinum* Zone: here and in the succeeding zone the small species *Actinocamax verus* is common, while *Gonioteuthis granulata* is found in the *Marsupites testudinarius* Zone; above this belemnites become rare in the Wealden District. Apart from various species of *Inoceramus*, which are of zonal value, the lamellibranchs of the Upper Chalk are mainly long ranging forms and include *Lopha semiplana*, *Plagiostoma hoperi*, *Chlamys cretosa* and *Spondylus spinosus*.

The cliffs of Kent and Sussex provide excellent sections of the Upper Chalk, but the beds are more accessible in the many pits and quarries inland, even though a large number have fallen into disuse in recent years.

# 5. Strata Exposed at the Surface—Tertiary Systems

Toward the end of the Cretaceous period earth-movements caused a major regression of the Chalk sea over much of north-west Europe, thus ending the Mesozoic era and commencing the Tertiary, the third geological era. These earth-movements, the first rumblings of the Alpine orogeny, initiated the Wealden uplift and converted all the Wealden District into a land area, probably of low relief surrounded by a shallow shelf-sea.

In the earlier part of the Tertiary era, during Eocene and Oligocene times, the sea alternately encroached upon and retreated from the new land arca which was being intermittently uplifted as the orogeny gathered force. Evidence of these uplifts lies in the presence of Lower Greensand ehert pebbles probably derived from the Weald which occur in ten Tertiary deposits from late Eocene times onward, indicating that subaeriahl erosio of the Weald had cut down as far as the Lower Greensand. These movements, the outer fringe of those which, farther south, were producing mountain ranges stretching from the Alps to the Himalayas, culminated in late Oligocene or early Miocene times in the formation of the Wealden structures as we know them today.

The last of the Tertiary systems, the Pliocene, is marked by a readvance of the sea on to the edges of the Wealden uplift.

The end of the Mesozoic era was marked by several important changes in the fauna and flora which, in the Tertiary, began for the first time to bear some resemblance to those of today. True birds such as *Argillornis* replaced the winged reptiles and, with the extinction of the group of great reptiles the placental mammals gained ascendency, leaving only a few reptiles such as the crocodiles, turtles and snakes to continue to the present day. In the sea the ammonites and belemnites became extinct and the invertebrate stock became generally more akin to that of the present. On land the grasses, an important element in modern floras, first appeared during Eocene times.

Despite the great lithological contrast between the Chalk and the clastic sediments of the Tertiary systems the unconformity between them is not angular and can only be seen by comparing the Chalk zones present immediately beneath the unconformity at various localities. The greatest observable difference in our area is between the Chatham and Chichester districts, where the Eocene rests on the zones of *Micraster cortestudinarium* and *Gonioteuthis quadrata* respectively. Thus, in a distance of some 60 miles there is a difference in level of only 400 ft of Chalk. A further complication is that the lowest Eocene in the north-west Kent area (Thanet Beds) is older than that in the south Sussex area (Reading Beds) where higher Chalk zones are preserved; it is therefore possible that in the latter area a complete Chalk sequence was originally present.

All the Tertiary systems except the Miocene are represented in Britain, but in our area only the lower part of the Eocene and part of the Pliocene are present.

## Eocene System

Although now separated into numerous tectonic basins by the Miocene earth-movements, the Eocene and Oligocene beds of north-west Europe were originally deposited in one large sedimentary basin, the Anglo-Franco-Belgium Basin. In England the Eocene occupies two synclinal areas, the London Basin and the Hampshire Basin, separated by the Wealden uplift and its westerly extension. Only the eastern extremity of each of these basins is present in our area, cropping out in north Kent and south-west Sussex respectively.

Within the depositional basin there are great lithological variations and facies changes from fluviatile to deltaic and from deltaic to marine can be traced away from the shorelines towards the centre. Throughout Eocene times the shoreline lay to the west of the Wealden District, which lay partly in the deltaic area (south-west Sussex) and partly in the open sea (north Kent). Furthermore, as Professor L. D. Stamp has shown, the positions of the shorelines varied considerably as the sea first advanced and then retreated in sympathy with the spasmodic subsidence and earth-movements which occurred throughout this period. Thus the Eocene is made up of a series of depositional cycles which begin with a marine transgression, usually represented by a coarse pebbly beach deposit. This passes up into finer marine sediments and often, when that particular part of the basin had become filled, into deltaic or fluviatile sands which are eventually capped by the basal pebble bed of the next cycle. Marine deposits also pass inland into fluviatile deposits so that in different areas deposits of the same age can have very dissimilar lithologies.

The fauna and flora of the Eocene frequently contains several distinct elements. In the marine environments endemic molluscs are mixed with terrestrial plant and vertebrate remains brought into the basin by strong river currents. In early Eocene (Landenian) times the flora indicates a temperate climate which changed gradually until London Clay (Ypresian) times when the land areas were fringed with lush sub-tropical vegetation.

The Eocene is subdivided into a number of stages based on the sedimentary cycles; only part of the Lower Eocene is present in our area.

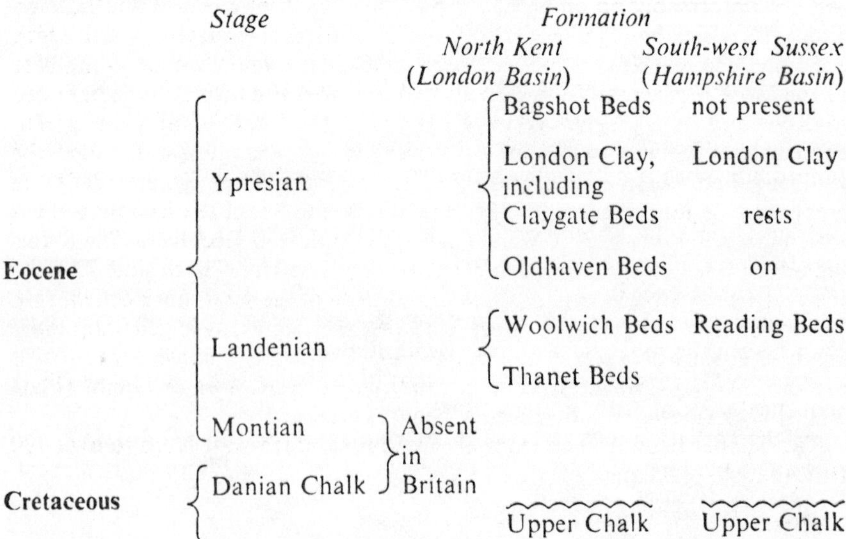

| | *Stage* | *Formation* North Kent (London Basin) | *Formation* South-west Sussex (Hampshire Basin) |
|---|---|---|---|
| **Eocene** | Ypresian | Bagshot Beds | not present |
| | | London Clay, including Claygate Beds | London Clay rests |
| | | Oldhaven Beds | on |
| | Landenian | Woolwich Beds | Reading Beds |
| | | Thanet Beds | |
| | Montian | Absent in Britain | |
| **Cretaceous** | Danian Chalk | Absent in Britain | |
| | | Upper Chalk | Upper Chalk |

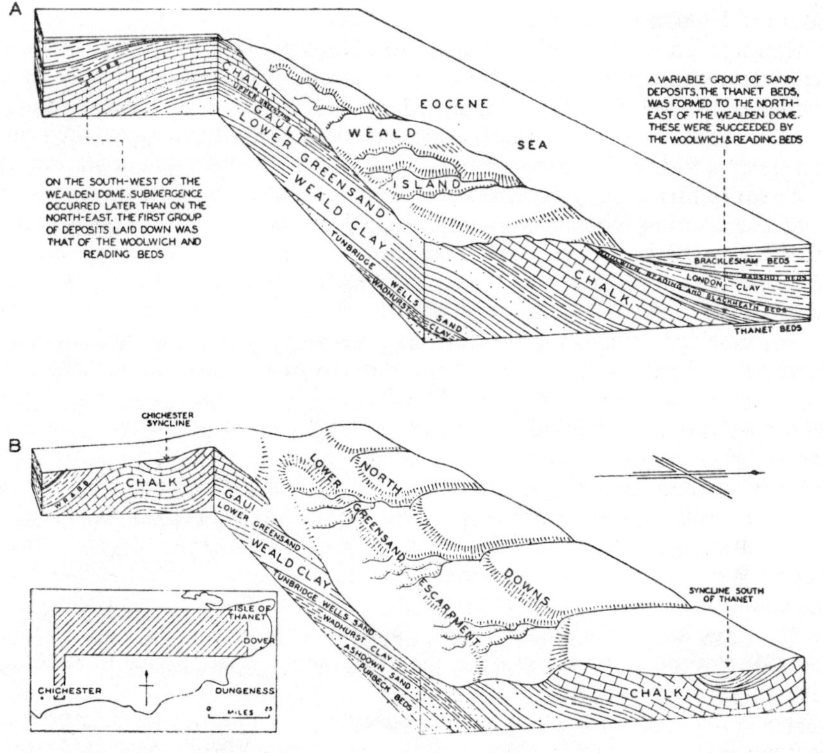


FIG. 9.

A. *Block diagram showing the arrangement of strata during Eocene times, and their relationship to the deposition of the Eocene beds*

B. *Block diagram showing present day arrangement of the strata*

*Thanet Beds*

The Thanet Beds are the earliest Eocene deposits in Britain and always rest unconformably on an eroded Chalk surface, locally in solution hollows and pipes which have the appearance of an angular unconformity but which are a post-Eocene feature formed by ground water circulation along the base of the more permeable Tertiary beds. In our area the formation is confined to Kent and its transgressive base is marked by a bed of unworn, green-coated flints set in a matrix of dark clay and glauconitic sand, called the Bullhead Bed. In the type area, the Isle of Thanet, the Thanet Beds are composed of fine, glauconitic, marine sands and fossiliferous sandy clays which are well exposed in the cliffs at Pegwell Bay and Reculver. The fossils include species of the lamellibranchs *Arctica*, *Astarte*, *Ostrea* and *Thracia*, the gastropods *Sigatica* and *Siphonalia* and teeth of the sand shark *Odontaspis*.

Farther west, towards the River Medway, the deposits are generally more sandy and probably formed in a shallow brackish-water environment: fossils are rare. Good exposures occur in sand pits such as those at Upnor (Plate VII B) near Chatham and at Sturry near Canterbury.

The Thanet Beds thicken from about 80 ft in north-west Kent to over 100 ft in the Isle of Thanet.

*Woolwich and Reading Beds*

The oldest Eocene deposits in south-west Sussex are well-bedded clays crowded with brackish-water shells (Woolwich Beds facies of the Reading Beds) and underlain by a marine pebble bed containing small, rolled, green-coated flints resting directly on the Chalk. This, the Reading Bottom Bed, represents the second important transgression of the Landenian. In the Newhaven area these clays are 30 ft thick, but farther west they thin rapidly and are overlain by coarse cross-bedded, fluviatile sands and mottled clays, the Reading Beds proper. Near Chichester the Reading Beds are about 90 ft thick, but exposures are rare, the outcrop being largely masked by Drift deposits.

In east Kent are glauconitic sands, in places clayey and containing pebbles, and generally about 25 ft thick. At some levels there are subordinate clay seams which represent a deltaic environment and contain various species of the lamellibranchs *Corbicula* and *Ostrea* and the gastropods '*Cerithium*' and *Melanopsis*. Good sections occur in the cliffs between Herne Bay and Reculver where a shell bed, the *Corbula* Bed, occurs at the base of the formation and contains myriads of the lamellibranch *Corbula regulbiensis* (N.B.—this bed is included in the Thanet Beds by some authors).

*Oldhaven Beds*

The base of the Ypresian cycle in north Kent is marked by a pebble bed, consisting of black flint pebbles in a buff or yellow sandy matrix, which cuts down into the underlying Woolwich Beds. This pebble bed and the overlying marine cross-bedded sands make up the Oldhaven Beds which then pass up conformably into the marine London Clay. At Herne Bay, where the formation is about 20 ft thick, shelly bands containing lamellibranchs and gastropods are common. In the Hampshire Basin, which lay farther from the sea than did east Kent during Landenian times, the Ypresian transgression occurred slightly later and the London Clay rests directly on the Reading Beds.

*London Clay*

The London Clay is lithologically very uniform and consists principally of marine clay, blue when fresh but weathering to brown. In Kent it crops out around Whitstable and in the Isle of Sheppey and can be seen in cliff sections at both localities. In Sussex outliers occur near Chichester, Bognor and Newhaven, where the London Clay rests on Reading Beds and is slightly more sandy than the deposits in Kent. At the base of the formation a thin pebble bed containing dark flints commonly occurs and at various horizons calcareous concretions, either in bands or as large nodules (cementstones or 'septaria'), are present. A shelly, calcareous sandstone, the Bognor Rock, is developed at Bognor.

Fossils are scarce in general but are common at certain horizons. The cementstones of the Isle of Sheppey in particular have yielded a large fauna which includes remains of the starfish *Astropecten crispatus*, the crab *Xanthopsis leachi*, the lobster *Hoploparia gammaroides*, the snake *Palaeophis toliapicus*, fish including *Sparnodus bowerbanki*, species of the turtles *Lytoloma* and *Trionyx* and many molluscs. These include the lamellibranchs *Phola-*

*domya dixoni*, *Glycymeris brevirostris* and *Pinna affinis* and the gastropod *Athleta* (*Volutospina*) *denudatus*. Fossil wood, containing calcareous tubes of the wood-boring lamellibranch *Teredo* is also of frequent occurrence.

In the Bognor area plant remains are rare, but the cliffs of the Isle of Sheppey are famous for the large variety of fruits and seeds which they have yielded. Very few specimens have been found *in situ* in the cliffs as they are much more readily visible when winnowed into pockets on the foreshore by wave-action. The flora includes fruits of the stemless palm *Nipa burtini*, berries of the cinnamon and seeds of the magnolia.

In the Isle of Sheppey the London Clay is about 480 ft thick; in the Hampshire Basin it is 300 ft, but only the lowest 100 ft is exposed in our area.

*Bagshot and Claygate Beds*

Near Minster, in the Isle of Sheppey, two outliers of Bagshot Beds, composed of fine buff sand with flint pebbles, are separated from the London Clay by 12 ft of transitional sand and clay, the Claygate Beds.

## Pliocene and Early Pleistocene Deposits

Sands exposed in solution ' pipes ' in the Chalk, in quarries at the crest of the North Downs at Lenham in Kent, at about 600 ft above O.D., have attracted attention since 1854, when they were found to contain blocks of ferruginous sandstone crowded with fossils preserved in the form of moulds. Patches of similar sand, with some fossiliferous sandstone, were also found on the summit-plateau of the Downs nearby. The sands are fine grained and for the most part bright red, pink or yellow, and more rarely pale grey. Only in a few of the pipes has their original stratification been preserved. The fossils have been proved to be of Coralline Crag age (i.e. they belong to the late Pliocene, the last epoch of the Tertiary era). The deposits are named the Lenham Beds. They correspond in type to sands developed on the opposite side of the North Sea, near Diest and Antwerp, and are therefore also given the name ' Diestian.'

Similar fossiliferous sandstone has been found on the South Downs near Beachy Head, and deposits of sand at about 500 to 600 ft O.D. occur at many places on the North Downs. In east Kent, where they rest on a platform tilted towards the north-east, the sands are generally red or brown; it is seldom possible to draw a definite line between these sands and the Clay-with-flints. North of Reigate are numerous detached patches of sand and shingle, much masked by the overlying Clay-with-flints. Disturbed deposits at Netley Heath near Guildford have yielded Red Crag (i.e. early Pleistocene) fossils.

Many of these deposits have been shown to contain similar heavy minerals, and though this does not imply their exact equivalence of age it supports the conclusion that they are remnants of a formerly much more extensive spread of sand. The sea on the floor of which they were laid down presumably advanced westwards, since the deposits at Lenham are older than those at Netley Heath. A surface that appears to have been eroded by this sea as it advanced, since all the scattered deposits lie on it, now bevels the top of the North Downs. The form of this surface suggests that the central part of the Weald stood as an island in the sea, and that a line of summits in the central part of the North Downs, culminating at Botley Hill near Sevenoaks, 882 ft above O.D., formed part of the island, as did the higher parts of Leith Hill, Hindhead Common and Black Down in the western Weald, and many of the summits of the South Downs.

The fossils most frequently found in the Lenham Beds are the lamellibranchs *Cardium* (*Acanthocardia*) aff. *andreae* and *Nucula sulcata*. *Barbatia* (*Diluvarca*) *diluvii* also occurs. Gastropods are numerous, and one species of the brachiopod *Terebratula* is represented. The polyzoan *Cupuladria canariensis* is common.

# 6. Structure

Although the present day surface structures of the Wealden District were formed during late Oligocene or early Miocene times, the history of the Wealden uplift goes back to near the beginning of the Mesozoic era and what we now see is only the climax of a process spanning 150 million years.

During the Palaeozoic two major orogenies affected north-west Europe. The effect of the first, the Caledonian orogeny, has been recognized in our area only by the unconformity between the Silurian and the Devonian. The second, the Hercynian orogeny, is better known and produced structures having a roughly east-south-easterly trend of which the synclinal Kent Coalfield basin is the best example in the area. Within the sub-Mesozoic floor of the Weald the main fold trends are thought to conform to this Hercynian direction but at present insufficient borehole evidence has been obtained either to confirm or disprove this hypothesis. Professor H. Stille has coined the names Palaeoeurope to describe that part of northern Europe in which Caledonian folding is the dominant structural feature, and Mesoeurope for the central European area in which Hercynian folds predominate. He has further suggested that the junction of these two tectonic provinces runs approximately through the central Weald in an east-west direction, the Kent Coalfield lying to the north of the junction and within Palaeoeurope.

At the close of the Palaeozoic era the Wealden District existed as a platform of folded rocks in which a shallow depression formed in late Triassic times (Fig. 10, stage I). Further downwarping along the line of this depression, accompanied by complementary uplift along its margins (stage II) continued until mid-Cretaceous times when differential subsidence effectively ceased (stage III), although minor differences in the thickness of the Chalk may represent the final phases of this movement. In the central part of our area there is little evidence to suggest the occurrence of the earth-movements, the forerunners of the Alpine orogeny, which elsewhere in Europe occurred at intervals throughout the Jurassic and Cretaceous periods. Along the margins of the basin of deposition these movements are better seen, being marked by regressions and transgressions of the shorelines.

The first phase of the Alpine earth-movements to affect the whole Weald occurred in late Cretaceous (Danian) or early Eocene (Montian) times and, although producing few structures, it probably raised much of the area above sea-level for the first time since the Triassic period. The main Alpine movements, occurring in late Oligocene or early Miocene times, were followed by epeirogenic movements which have continued to the present day and which have raised the area by 500 ft since the beginning of the Pleistocene.

Thus, the structural history of the Wealden District can be divided into three phases: a pre-Mesozoic period culminating in a platform of folded Palaeozoic rocks, a Mesozoic period of downwarping and sedimentation and, thirdly, a period of Tertiary uplift and folding. The exact relationship between the Hercynian folding, the axis of the Mesozoic sedimentary trough and the axis of the Wealden uplift, which all have roughly the same alignment,

STAGE I The early Mesozoic sea invades the Palaeozoic platform and the Mesozoic trough begins to form

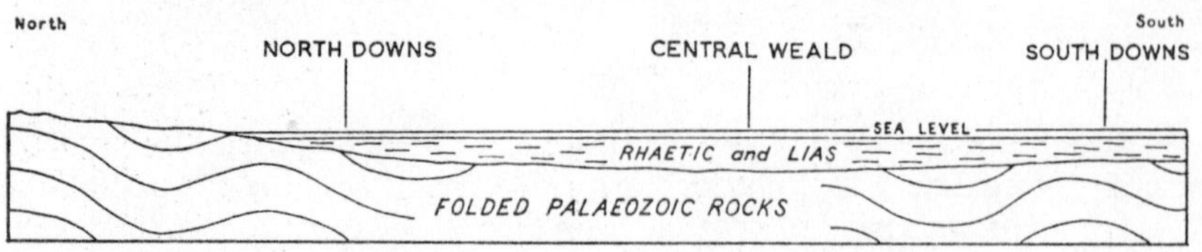


STAGE II Subsidence of the trough continues throughout Jurassic and early Cretaceous times with sporadic emergence of the margins of the trough in the north

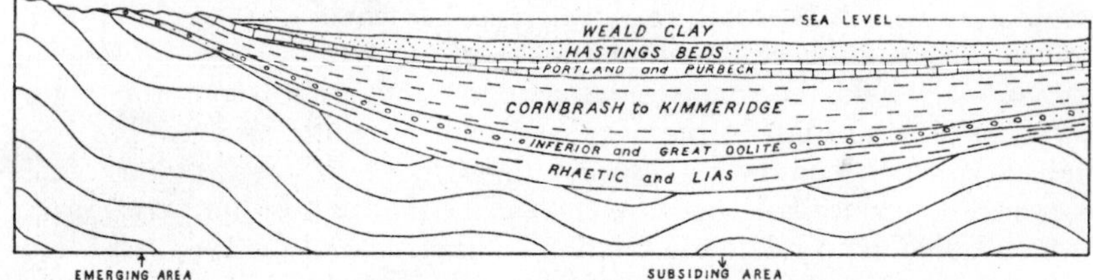


STAGE III Differential subsidence ceases and the London Uplands are submerged beneath the Gault and later Cretaceous transgressions

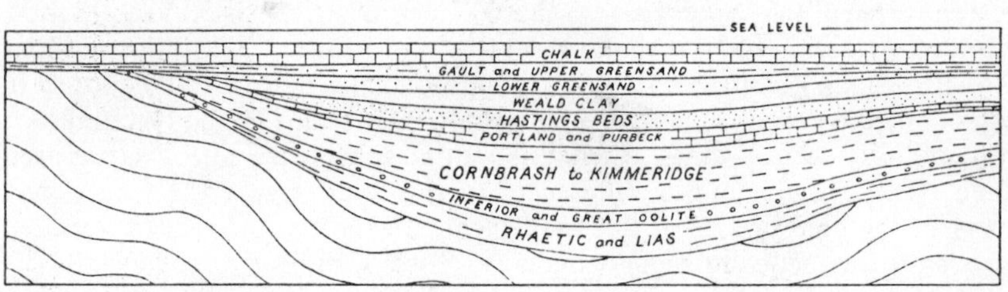


STAGE IV Tertiary folding and subsequent subaerial erosion produce the present day structure and topography

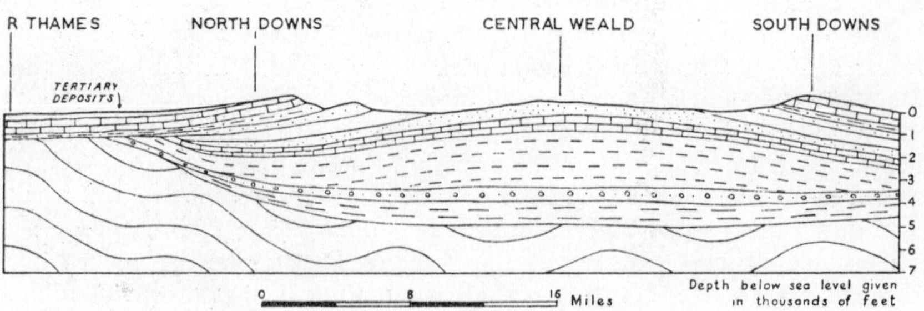


FIG. 10. *Sections illustrating the structural evolution of the Wealden uplift.* (Line of section approximately London to Brighton)

Some Characteristic Fossils from the Chalk

**1.** *Micraster coranguinum* Leske; **2.** *Phymosoma koenigi* (Mantell); **3.** *Terebratulina lata* Etheridge; **4.** *Actinocamax plenus* (Blainville); **5.** *Inoceramus lamarcki* Parkinson; **6.** *Marsupites testudinarius* (Schlotheim); **7.** *Ptychodus latissimus* Agassiz; **8.** *Schloenbachia subvarians* Spath.

(*For full explanation see p. x*)

(A.78

A. Quarry in Upper Chalk, Frindsbury, Kent

B. Section in Lower Eocene Deposits, Upnor, Kent

(*For full explanation see p. x*)

(A.78

is not known. That the subsidiary folds within the uplift, and possibly the western part of the uplift itself, have been controlled by the position of the trough is beyond doubt. Whether the position of the trough has itself been controlled by the Hercynian folds and whether these folds have posthumously controlled the Alpine folding is uncertain, although this last possibility seems unlikely. Certainly the inter-relationship of these three trends in the structure of the area is a remarkable coincidence, but until detailed information has been obtained about the nature of the folding in the sub-Mesozoic floor no closer analysis of this relationship can be made. A further possibility is that the Alpine earth-movements were strong enough to impose their normal east-west trend upon the area and that they were assisted by having structures with this trend already present in the sub-Mesozoic floor.

The Wealden uplift is a large, shallow, domal structure, 135 miles long and a maximum of 50 miles wide, stretching from the Bas Boulonnais in northern France through Kent, Sussex and Surrey to the Hampshire Downs. At the eastern end of the structure the Boulonnais is separated from the remainder of the dome by the English Channel. Regional dips away from the axis of the fold are very low, being only one to two degrees, but in numerous subsidiary folds which complicate the uplift, much steeper dips are locally present. Although the main fold is roughly symmetrical, some of the minor folds show a marked asymmetry, the anticlines having a steeper north-facing limb in accord with the main orogenic pressure which lay to the south in the region of the Alps. West of Ashdown Forest the axis of the main fold runs east-west, swinging to E.S.E.–W.N.W. east of this area to become parallel to the margin of the Mesozoic sedimentary trough. In the eastern part of the area nearly all the faults and subsidiary folds (Fig. 11) also show this change of trend and structures are noticeably absent to the north-east of a line from Maidstone to Folkestone which marks approximately the edge of the stable Palaeozoic platform (p. 6). Undoubtedly the presence of competent Palaeozoic rocks near the surface inhibited the formation of folds in this area; conversely, the more important folds occur where the Mesozoic sediments are thickest. This feature is particularly well demonstrated by the folds affecting the Chalk; these are restricted to the western part of the North Downs and to the South Downs (Fig. 12), both of which overlie a thick Mesozoic sequence.

The subsidiary structures at the surface in the Wealden District can be divided into three distinct zones, each zone dependent upon the lithology of the rocks in which it occurs. In the central Weald the outcrop of the Hastings Beds is characterized by long sinuous fault belts, between which there are large areas of unfolded or gently folded rocks; this area is surrounded by the relatively unfolded and unfaulted shales and mudstones of the Weald Clay in which the stresses were absorbed by bedding-plane slip. Surrounding both these zones the competent Lower Greensand and Chalk were folded with little fracturing, the intervening Gault behaving, but to a lesser extent, in the same manner as the Weald Clay.

Within the Hastings Beds the structures present again reflect the competence of the beds involved. The main outcrops of the massive sandstones of the Ashdown Sand occur in three unfaulted, shallow anticlinal culminations *en échelon* bounded by large faults which involve the shales of the Wadhurst

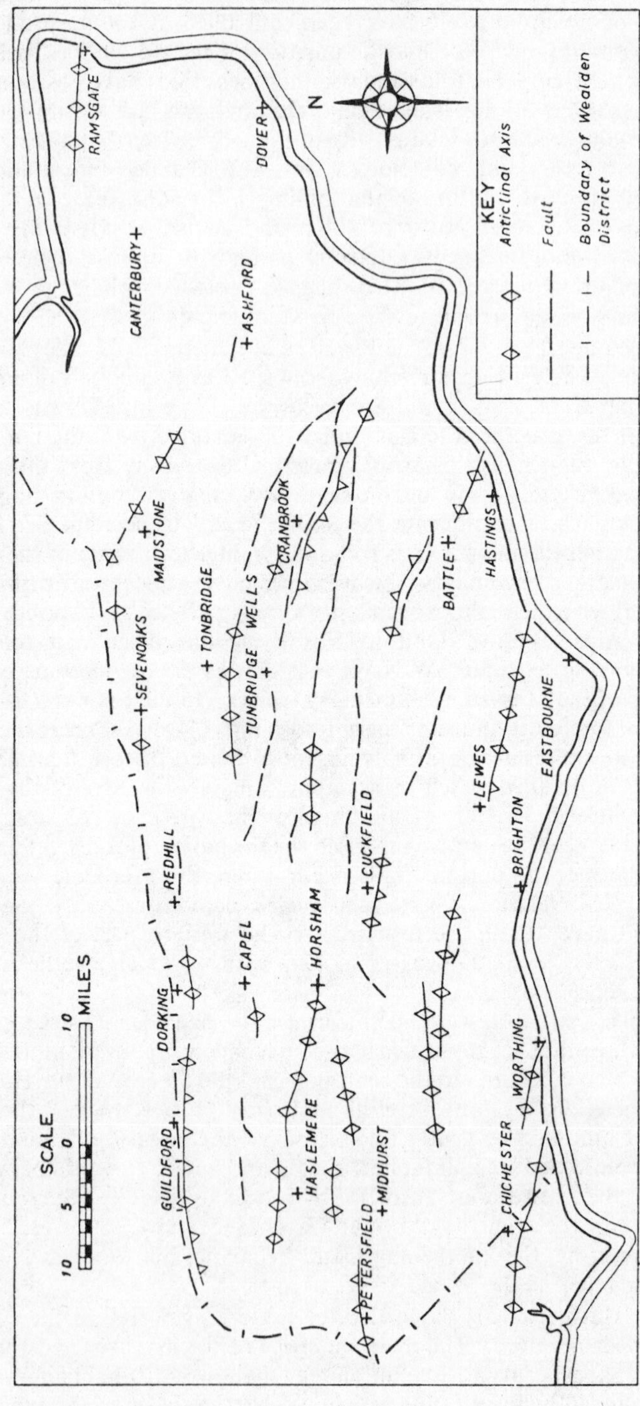


FIG. 11. *Sketch-map showing the main trends of anticlinal folding and the major fault lines in the Wealden District*

Clay. These faults follow the trend of the main fold closely (Plate I and Fig. 11) and significant examples which depart appreciably from this trend are very rare. Many of the faults are confined to narrow, well-defined belts bounded by two sub-parallel, normal faults which can often be traced for many miles and which may have displacements of up to 500 ft. Within the intervening area, which is usually downfaulted and which may be a quarter to half mile in width, the strata often have steep dips and are disturbed by numerous small faults and occasional thrusts. These large fault belts are probably complex, crestal tension faults and may have been formed along reactivated Hercynian fault lines in the sub-Mesozoic floor. Much of this area is underlain by 3000 ft to 5000 ft of Mesozoic sediments which would account for the sinuous nature of these faults at the surface. Shallow anticlines occur near Fairlight, Brightling, Cranbrook and Penshurst, but they are less significant in governing the shape of the outcrops than are the faults.

Few major folds or faults affect the Weald Clay, except in the immediate vicinity of the junctions with the Hastings Beds and the Lower Greensand, and the outcrop is singularly uncomplicated by comparison with that of the Hastings Beds. Furthermore, there are neither inliers of Hastings Beds within the Weald Clay outcrop nor outliers of Weald Clay within the Hastings Beds outcrop; it seems that the two formations behaved almost independently of one another when folded. This hypothesis is partially confirmed by the presence of major faulting along much of the boundary between them and faults having large displacements in the Hastings Beds can in places be shown to die out on passing into the Weald Clay. It is possible that during folding, movement occurred along numerous slip planes in the lower part of the Weald Clay, thus allowing the bulk of it to move over the Hastings Beds independently.

The strata between the Lower Greensand and the Eocene behaved as a single coherent unit and are flexed into similar folds, several of which are asymmetrical. The best example of this asymmetry is the Hogs Back fold, a monocline running along the North Downs from Farnham to Guildford and Dorking. The steepest visible part of the fold occurs in the lower part of the Chalk and near Farnham this horizon dips at 45° to 55°. Along much of its length the fold is complicated by strike faults which, near Guildford and Runfold, replace the steep limb of the fold (Fig. 13). Numerous small dip faults are also present.

Along the South Downs there are three important sub-parallel lines of folding in which a syncline is associated with a complementary anticline (Fig. 12). Between Worthing, Arundel and Chichester Eocene deposits are preserved in the core of a syncline which is bounded on its southern side by an anticline in the Chalk. Similarly, near Lewes, an anticline running parallel to and south of the Mount Caburn syncline, brings up the Upper Greensand in the Ouse gap. South of Henfield a large anticline in the Weald Clay runs east-west, its northern limb being folded into a syncline which runs through the village itself.

In north Kent a shallow syncline containing Eocene deposits runs along the Wantsum Strait, south of the Isle of Thanet.

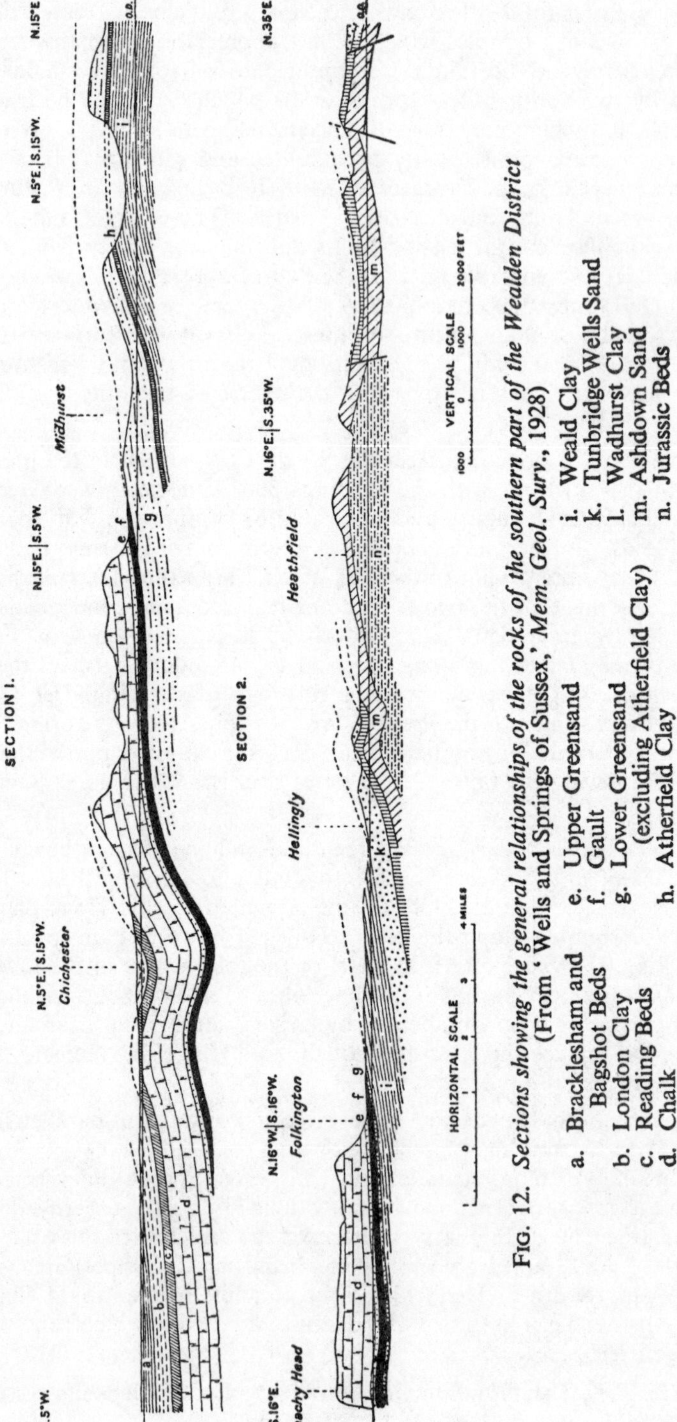


FIG. 12. *Sections showing the general relationships of the rocks of the southern part of the Wealden District* (From 'Wells and Springs of Sussex,' *Mem. Geol. Surv.*, 1928)

a. Bracklesham and Bagshot Beds
b. London Clay
c. Reading Beds
d. Chalk
e. Upper Greensand
f. Gault
g. Lower Greensand (excluding Atherfield Clay)
h. Atherfield Clay
i. Weald Clay
k. Tunbridge Wells Sand
l. Wadhurst Clay
m. Ashdown Sand
n. Jurassic Beds

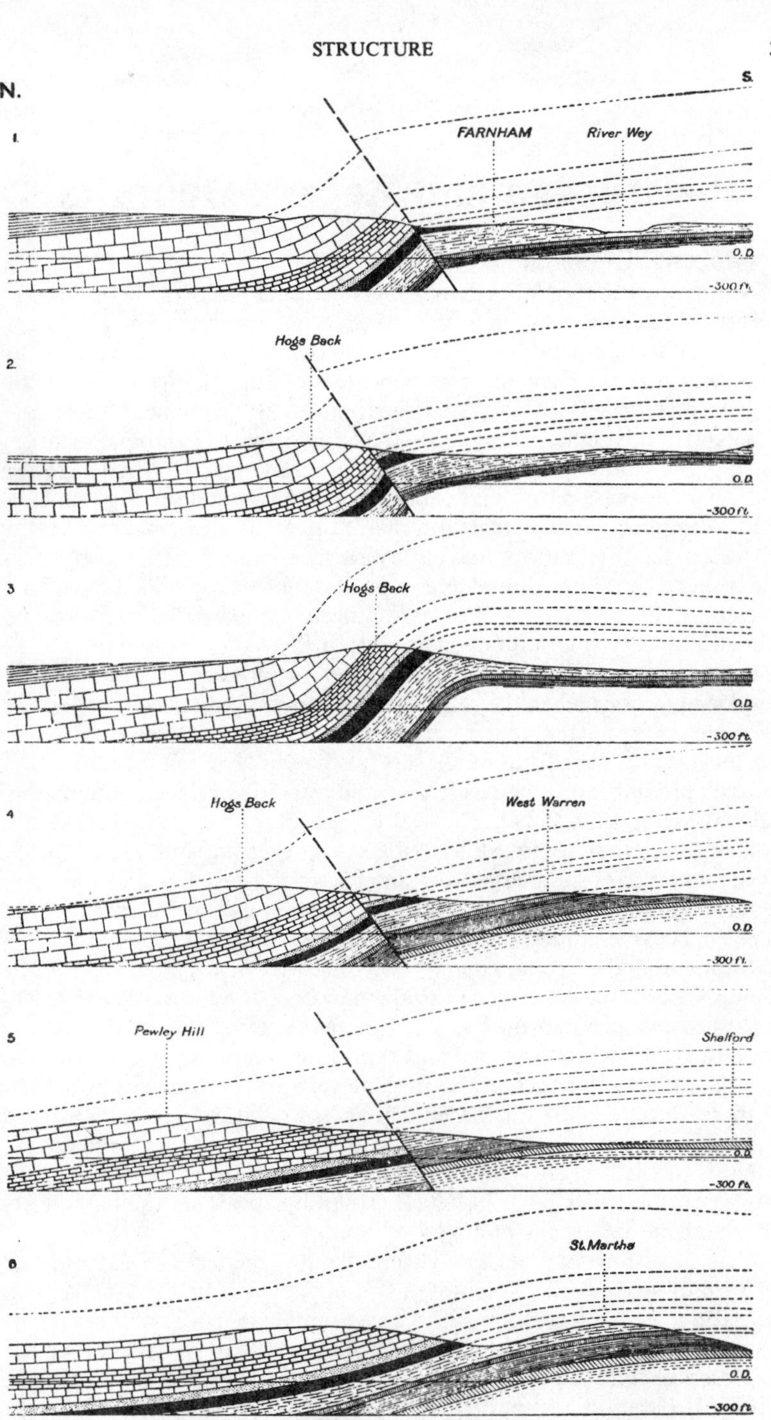


FIG. 13. *Transverse sections of the Hogs Back fold*
(From 'Geology of the Country around Aldershot and Guildford,' *Mem. Geol. Surv.*, 1929)

# 7. Pleistocene and Recent Deposits

## Pleistocene Deposits

The molluscan fauna of the early Pleistocene deposits of the North Downs indicates a cooler climate than that of the Pliocene, heralding the oncoming of the Pleistocene glaciation which, at its maximum, was to cover the whole of Britain north of the River Thames beneath a continental ice-sheet. Although no glaciers reached the Wealden District, small permanent snow and ice fields capped the higher parts of the Chalk and Lower Greensand escarpments and over the whole of the area the ground was perennially frozen to a great depth. Under these periglacial conditions underground see page (p. 84), now the most important single factor in the drainage of the area, could not occur and meltwater was removed solely by surface run-off. This resulted in the formation of certain erosional and depositional features which have no exact counterpart at the present day, particularly on the Chalk outcrop where there is now only intermittent surface drainage.

Three major glaciations are recognized in Britain, separated by warm interglacial periods when the rainfall was probably enhanced and denudation was rapid. During the colder phases of the period vast amounts of water were locked up in the form of ice so that the sea-level fell, at times to 300 ft below its present level; conversely, in the warm interglacial periods the sea-level was higher than today. Most of the features produced by these eustatic changes have been removed by subsequent erosion, but along the South Coast remnants of submerged forests, raised sea-beaches and old sea-cliffs are still preserved. Inland there is more evidence. In the interglacial periods the rivers became graded to a high sea-level so that, with the onset of colder conditions and the accompanying fall in sea-level, they began to cut their valleys deeper to become graded to the new base-level, leaving patches of the older alluvium perched on the sides of the new valley. In the next warm period the valleys were drowned and deposition again took place. In southern England these glacial fluctuations in sea-level are superimposed upon a steady fall in sea-level relative to the land that has occurred since Pliocene times (when it was approximately 600 ft higher than at the present day). The remnants of the successive alluvial flood plains of the rivers form a series of terraces on the valley sides in which, generally speaking, the highest are the oldest and the lowest the youngest.

During Pleistocene times the first undisputed evidence of Man appears in the form of stone tools, generally made of flint, which are usually found in association with terrace deposits. These implements are the most durable legacy of Man's early existence and are usually the only evidence we have of his presence. Consequently, our knowledge and the classification of early cultures is based almost entirely on the study of stone tools. Three groups of prehistoric cultures are recognized. The Palaeolithic (Old Stone Age) is confined to the Pleistocene period when Man occupied caves and lived by hunting: some examples of tools of this period are shown in Fig. 15. The Mesolithic (Middle Stone Age) and Neolithic (New Stone Age) periods are both of Holocene (Recent) age, the Neolithic being characterized by polished stone tools and basic crafts of early civilisation such as agriculture, stock-breeding, pottery manufacture and weaving.

Most of the deposits of Pleistocene and Holocene age in our area are products of the subaerial denudation of the solid formations on which they rest unconformably. These deposits are termed ' Drifts ' and may be classified on a genetic basis into three broad categories, Head deposits, River deposits and Beach deposits.

The Pleistocene–Recent boundary is taken at the end of the last major European glaciation, which roughly corresponds to the replacement of the Palaeolithic by the Mesolithic culture approximately 10 000 years ago. In the Wealden District there is little evidence to distinguish this last cold period from those immediately before and after it. Flint implements are rare and are almost exclusively confined to terrace deposits. Insufficient radiocarbon datings have yet been carried out on drift deposits in the Weald to enable the boundary between Pleistocene and Recent deposits to be fixed in any but the most general manner. Furthermore, most of the drifts described below have been forming sporadically but continuously since early Pleistocene times and only a comparative history of them, deduced from an examination of their relative levels and relationships to one another, can be obtained.

In the simplified table overleaf only the more important periods of formation of head are shown.

**Head Deposits**

Head deposits are drifts produced by solifluxion, a process in which water acts as a lubricant rather than as an agent of transport. All gradations between Head and River deposits occur, so that it is often difficult to draw a precise line between the two. Head deposits are characteristically made up of poorly sorted, angular materials of local derivation. Stratification, if present, is generally poor and the upper and lower surfaces of the deposits, unlike those of River deposits are rarely horizontal. At the present day, downwash and soil-creep account for the main types of head being formed and they are classified together as undifferentiated head. Small amounts of material which have formed by solifluxion processes from other drifts occur throughout the area but are of minor importance.

*Clay-with-flints*

Clay-with-flints occurs extensively on the higher parts of the Chalk dip-slopes, particularly on the North Downs. The deposits formerly extended as an almost continuous sheet, but now only dissected remnants of the original spread remain. As the name implies, flints and clay constitute the bulk of the deposit, but a mixture containing gravel, sand and loam is present in many localities. The base of the Clay-with-flints is commonly irregular and locally occupies solution pockets and pipes in the Chalk. The flints occur in assorted shapes and sizes, in varying states of weathering, and are usually set in the clay in a haphazard manner.

The origin of the Clay-with-flints is varied. W. Whitaker, who first described the deposit, suggested that it was left as a residue by solution of the Chalk and that it is likely to be of many ages and may even be forming

| | | Head Deposits | River Deposits | Beach Deposits |
|---|---|---|---|---|
| Holocene | Neolithic to Present Day | Modern downwash and earlier solifluxion deposits | Modern alluvium and peat<br>Buried river channel deposits | Modern shingle and windblown sand<br>Submerged forests and beaches<br>Older shingle |
| | Mesolithic | Brickearth and Coombe Deposits | 1st Terrace (River Medway) | |
| Pleistocene | Palaeolithic | Older brickearth, solifluxion and Coombe Deposits | Higher terraces of River Medway | 15-Foot Beach<br>100-Foot Beach |
| | | Clay-with-flints<br>Plateau drift | | 500-Foot Beach (Netley Heath) |

Not to Scale

at the present day. The theory is inadequate as a whole, for, although the deposit rests on a solution surface, mere solution of the Chalk could produce neither the necessary amount of clay, nor the correct proportion of clay to flints. Furthermore, in several localities in the Weald a major proportion of the material consists of remanié Eocene and Pliocene beds which could not have been derived by this means.

The Clay-with-flints, therefore, is probably the result of more than one process acting on deposits of several ages. Some was undoubtedly formed by solution of the Chalk, but the greater part, made up of nodular flints from the Chalk, sand from the Thanet Beds, clay from the Reading Beds and London Clay, pebbles of Eocene age and large flint cobbles and sand possibly

Characteristic Eocene Fossils

**1.** *Ostrea bellovacina* Lamarck; **2.** *Panopea intermedia* (J. Sowerby); **3.** *Corbula regulbiensis* Morris; **4.** *Cucullaea decussata* Parkinson; **5.** *Xanthopsis bispinosa* McCoy; **6.** a, b, c. *Odontaspis macrota striata* (Winkler); **7.** a, b. *Nemocardium plumsteadianum* (J. Sowerby); **8.** a, b. *Arctica morrisi* (J. de C. Sowerby); **9.** *Glycymeris brevirostris* (J. de C. Sowerby).

(*For full explanation see p. x*)

(A.3359

A. Submerged Forest of Little Galley Hill, Bexhill, Sussex

B. Junction of Folkestone Beds and Gault at Copt Point, Folkestone

(*For full explanation see p. x-xi*)

(A.5394)

(A.8321)

A. Superficial Structures in Weald Clay, Southwater, Sussex

B. Folkestone Warren Landslip, Folkestone, Kent

(*For full explanation see p. xi*)

(Photo: British Railways, Southern Region)

A. Coombe Deposits and Dry Valley and Nailbourne Deposits at Black Rock, Brighton (A

B. Meanders in the River Cuckmere, West Dean, Sussex.

(*For full explanation see p. xi*)

(A

derived from Pliocene deposits, is more likely to have been assembled under periglacial conditions, as a mélange of local materials disturbed and partly re-sorted by local ice-caps or snowfields.

The Clay-with-flints of the South Downs contains less material derived from Tertiary beds and a greater amount of unworn Chalk flints than that of the North Downs.

*Angular Chert Drift*

The higher ground of the Lower Greensand hills of Surrey and Kent is capped by angular chert rubble set in a sandy matrix, the whole deposit being derived from the Lower Greensand.

*Coombe Deposits*

Coombe Deposits, as their name implies, are a particular type of drift usually found in association with the coombes of the Chalk escarpments. They also occur however in hollows on the scarp-slopes and dip-slopes and in places have spread on to the outcrops of the Gault and Tertiary beds. The most important development of Coombe Deposits occurs on the southern slopes of the South Downs, where thicknesses up to 80 ft have been recorded, resting on both Chalk and Eocene beds.

The deposits are white or pale grey and are composed of angular and sub-angular blocks and smaller fragments of chalk set in a matrix of chalk mud. Angular flints are usually present and also occasional sandstone sarsens of Eocene age, the whole deposit having been very locally derived. The deposits are poorly sorted and are generally roughly stratified, a zone of decalcification, composed of up to 3 ft of brown flinty clay, frequently capping them. In some cases Coombe Deposits have been later cemented, by re-precipitation of the chalk, into a hard mass to form ' Coombe Rock.'

Although there were undoubtedly several periods of formation of Coombe Deposits it is thought that the greater part of the deposits was formed during a relatively short period of time at the close of the Glacial period. Under the periglacial conditions then existing the ground was frozen to a considerable depth so that the soft, porous beds of today acted as hard, impervious strata. During warmer intervals the surface layers thawed, and sludges of water, soil and subsoil slipped from the higher slopes, covering large areas of the lower ground (Fig. 14).

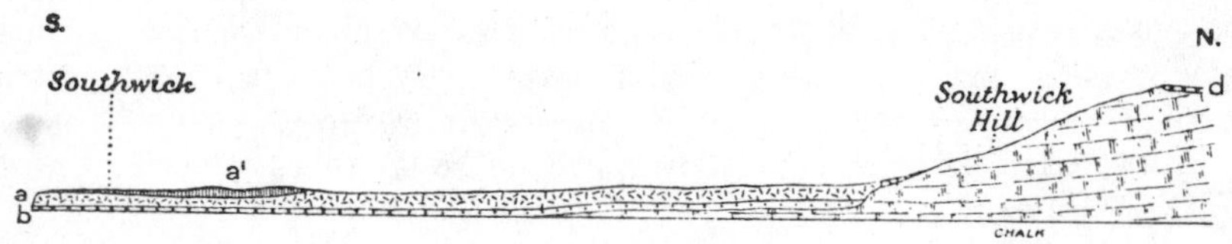


FIG. 14. *Diagrammatic section showing the arrangement of Pleistocene deposits near Portslade*

(After Prestwich, J. 1892, *Quart. J. Geol. Soc.*, **48**).

a[1]. Brickearth or Loam. a. Coombe Deposit. b. Raised Beach. d. Clay-with-Flints.

Coombe Deposits are well exposed in cliff sections between Brighton and Eastbourne, particularly at Black Rock, Brighton (Plate XI A) and at Birling Gap. At Black Rock the Coombe Deposits mask an earlier Pleistocene sea cliff and contain remains of the mammoth *Mammuthus primigenius*, and the woolly rhinoceras *Coelodonta antiquitatis*, both indicative of a cold climate.

*Brickearths*

In many localities in the Weald there occur deposits of buff, structureless loam or silt to which the name Brickearth has been given, since the material is eminently suitable for brickmaking. These brickearths have resulted from more than one process and, whilst they are mainly of Late or Post-glacial age, they are grouped together as a distinct lithological rock-type and do not form a stratigraphical unit. Most of them are a type of head deposit.

In lithology and mode of occurrence a few brickearths closely resemble the loess deposits of northern Europe and may be wind-borne; others probably accumulated in shallow water during a period of dry climatic conditions. Most of the brickearths contain scattered, small, angular stones and pockets of flint gravel and are so contaminated by locally derived materials that they have become argillaceous, sandy, stony or chalky. Such deposits may, in some cases, be the result of redistribution of earlier deposits by solifluxion or by widespread 'sheet-flooding' when the annual rainfall was far greater than at present; in extreme cases, such as the brickearths on the tracts of London Clay and Thanet Beds in north Kent the drift is hardly distinguishable from the solid.

Along the South Coast, notably near Hove, a third type of brickearth occurs which may be a fine-grained wash from the Downs which has been decalcified by long exposure to weathering processes: its thickness varies from a few inches to 15 ft.

*Head Gravel*

In north Kent spreads of gravel occur which are probably the remnants of sheets of head which formerly covered the gently sloping Chalk dip-slopes. They contain angular flints, subrounded flint cobbles and flint pebbles derived from Tertiary beds and it is possible that they represent deposits of several ages.

*Plateau Gravels*

Patches of gravel consisting of a few feet of roughly-bedded flint or chert in a clayey matrix occur at several localities in the Wealden District. As their name implies, they cap hilly ground and are unassociated with any present river-system, having been formed at some period before the main sequence of river gravels. In some cases they appear to be the relics of ancient sheets of Head Gravel.

**River Deposits**

*Dry Valley and Nailbourne Deposits*

Although none of the valleys of the Chalk dip-slopes contain permanent streams at the present day, many of them have flat floors underlain by partly water-laid deposits. These consist of calcareous flinty loams, sands with small flints or flint gravels depending upon the materials available in their immediate vicinity. The flints vary from angular to well-rounded and have commonly been derived from Tertiary beds or from high level gravels.

These deposits were formed at a time when the water table in the Chalk was higher than it is today and each valley contained a small permanent stream. Since then the water table has fallen and deposition occurs at the present time on a small scale only in those valleys retaining an intermittent stream or nailbourne.

In several sections along the South Coast, Dry Valley and Nailbourne Deposits can be seen to cut through Coombe Deposits, much of the former probably having been formed during the amelioration of climate which occurred after the cold period of Coombe Deposit deposition.

*River Gravels*

River Gravels have been recorded in association with all the major streams in the Wealden District, but no comprehensive classification has yet been devised which satisfactorily relates them either to one another or to the other drift deposits. Up to four main terrace levels are recognized on the larger rivers, with remnants of a fifth in some cases.

On the Hastings Beds outcrop the gravels are composed almost entirely of fragments of sandstone, mudstone, limestone and ironstone of local origin, but downstream, sandstone and chert pebbles from the Lower Greensand and flints from the Chalk predominate. Remains of mammoth, rhinoceras and reindeer and Palaeolithic flint implements have been found in several terraces, particularly those of the River Medway at Aylesford, the River Stour at Sturry and the River Wey near Farnham (Fig. 15).

In their lower reaches all the Wealden rivers possess buried channels which are now filled with alluvial deposits consisting of muds, sands and gravels. Near the coast these deposits are partly marine and in places they reach 100 ft in thickness.

*Alluvium*

Most of the River Alluvium of the area is fine grained and consists of muds, silts and fine sands deposited in stream flood plains. The alluvial flats, or ' levels,' near Pevensey, Lewes and Dungeness are made up of a composite type of alluvium consisting of both river and marine alluvium of slightly differing ages; the development of these features is discussed on p. 79.

## Beach Deposits

*Raised Sea-Beaches and Submerged Forests*

Remnants of raised sea-beaches have been recorded at about 100 ft and 15 ft above sea-level near the Sussex coast. Parts of the 100-Foot Beach are preserved between 70 ft O.D. and 130 ft O.D. on the dipslope of the Chalk between Chichester and Arundel. The beach is composed chiefly of flints with interbedded marine sands which have yielded a fauna indicating a warm climate. The deposit probably accumulated at a time of high sea-level during the last interglacial period of the Pleistocene. The lower, or 15-Foot Beach, rests on a platform in the Chalk and Eocene beds. This platform rises northwards to about 30 ft above O.D., at which height it is banked against

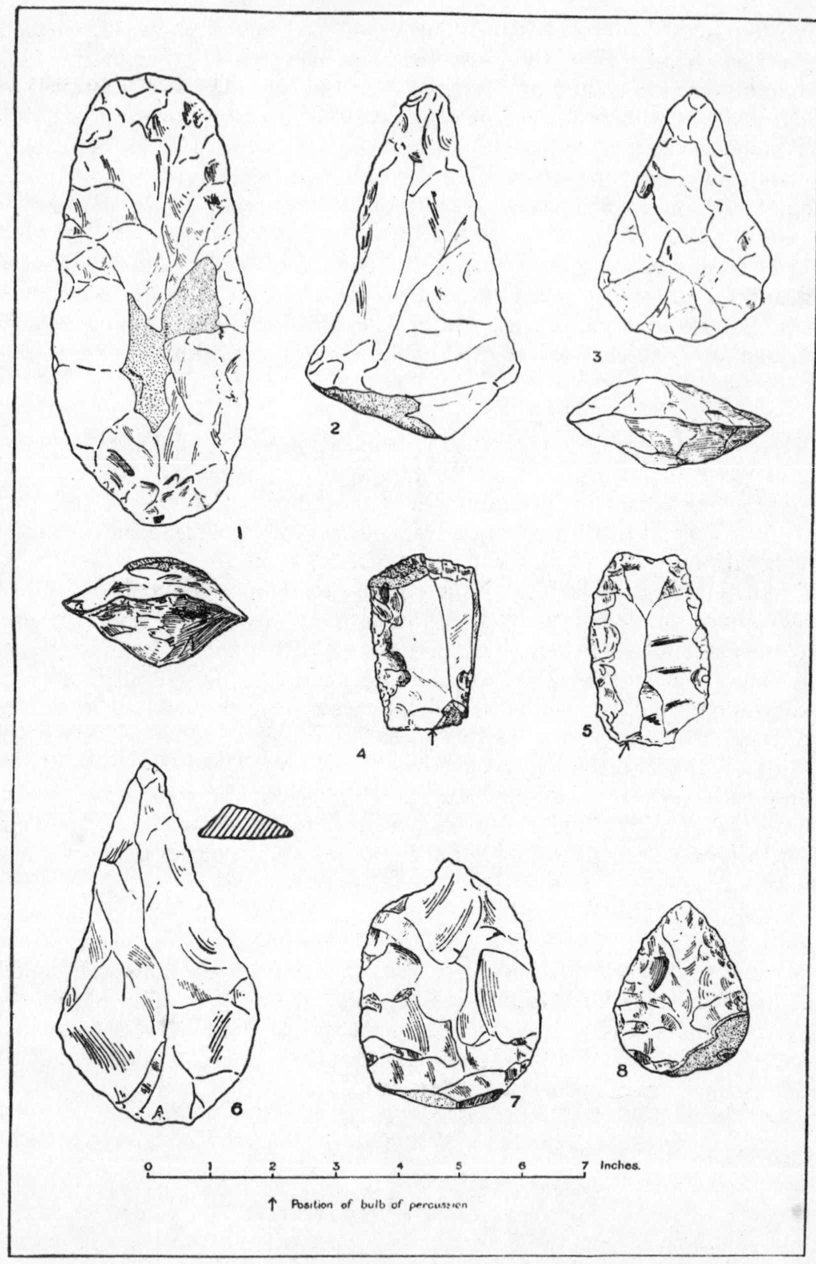


FIG. 15. *Palaeolithic implements from the terraced gravels at Farnham*
(From 'Geology of the Country around Aldershot and Guildford,' *Mem. Geol. Surv.*, 1929)

**1.** Sharp-rimmed ovate hand axe. Early Acheulean; **2.** Pointed hand axe. Middle Acheulean; **3.** Small pear-shaped hand axe. Middle Acheulean; **4.** Flake from flint, probably used as scraper. Probably Clactonian; **5.** As 4. Probably Clactonian; **6.** Triangular-section hand axe. Middle to Upper Acheulean; **7.** Thin discoidal implement. Levalloisian; **8.** Flat-sided scraping implement. Levalloisian.

an old cliff which marks the inner margin of the coastal plain. The cliff is now very degraded and is obscured by later Coombe Deposits and is only visible in the cliff section at Black Rock, Brighton. The beach consists of flint pebbles and marine sands and can be traced from Ferring to Brighton at approximately 15 ft O.D. beneath a cover of later drift deposits. Around Portslade (Fig. 14) it is preserved under Coombe Deposits, elsewhere beneath brickearth. Shells from the sandy lenses include the common mussel *Mytilus edulis* and the gastropod *Littorina littorea.* Correlation with the Portsmouth area suggests that the 15-Foot Beach was formed during the cold period immediately following the formation of the 100-Foot Beach.

Boles and trunks of trees belonging to a submerged forest can be seen at low tide on the wave-cut platform at Bexhill (Plate IX A), at Cliff End, near Hastings, and at Dover. This deposit was formed at a time when the sea level was 20 to 30 ft lower than at present and can probably be correlated with the Neolithic Forest Bed of Dungeness (p. 80). Although not a beach deposit they are a coastal feature associated with changes in sea-level and are grouped with raised beaches for convenience.

*Shingle*

Much of the Wealden coastline possesses a fringe of shingle, and in a few places accumulations of considerable extent are present. The shingle consists largely of flint pebbles, derived by marine erosion of the Chalk and Tertiary Beds, the latter in their turn having derived them from the Chalk. Small percentages of vein quartz, quartzite and quartz tourmaline grit similar to that occurring in south Devon are also present. All the above materials are carried eastwards along the South Coast by longshore drift due to the prevailing southwesterly winds.

The two most important accumulations of shingle in the area are at Langney Point (The Crumbles), near Eastbourne and at Dungeness. In both examples the shingle is aligned in sub-parallel ridges of differing ages, the older ridges generally being the farthest from the present shore. At Dungeness the highest ridges reach 20 ft O.D. and the shingle is up to 50 ft thick.

A prominent shingle bank runs along the east Kent coast from Kingsdown to Sandwich Bay, north of Deal; near Walmer it exeeds 200 yd in width and forms a protective apron to the line of old sea cliffs of Chalk.

*Blown Sand*

Only small amounts of blown sand occur around the coasts of the Wealden District. Near Camber hummocky dunes up to 50 ft high stretch for 1½ miles and there is a similar, but smaller, occurrence near Lydd. Small sand dunes have also been recorded on Pevensey Levels and in Sandwich Bay where they rest on older beach deposits.

# 8. Denudation and the Development of Scenery

## Denudational Processes

During Pliocene and early Pleistocene times the Weald proper existed as an island surrounded by the sea and undergoing subaerial denudation, which probably formed a drainage pattern largely concordant with the geological structures of the area. When the sea retreated the drainage on the freshly uncovered area ran straight downslope to the sea, cutting directly across structures in its path. This early drainage has subsequently been greatly modified by the Pleistocene glaciation and at the present day only the gaps in the Chalk escarpments of the North and South Downs bear any direct relationship to it.

The subaerial denudation of an area and the land forms which it produces is controlled by four main factors: (a) climatic conditions, (b) the position of sea-level relative to the land, (c) variations in the thicknesses and lithologies of the rocks involved and (d) the structures which affect those rocks. With the exception of the Chalk gaps mentioned above the land forms of the Wealden District have probably been produced since mid-Pleistocene times and only two climatic conditions need be considered, the periglacial climate of the Pleistocene cold periods and the temperate climate of the Pleistocene interglacials and of Recent times.

Periglacial climates are typified not only by their average low temperatures but also by numerous temperature fluctuations above and below freezing point. This latter effect causes frost-shattering, probably the most important single erosive agent in this type of weathering. The loose debris produced by it is carried away first by solifluxion processes and later by meltwater streams and rivers. Features attributable to periglacial weathering are rare in our area since they have usually been drastically modified or have been completely removed by later fluvial weathering. The best remaining examples are the coombes and dry valleys of the Chalk, where present day drainage is effected almost wholly by underground seepage and consequently little fluvial erosion takes place.

In periods of temperate climate mass-wasting, in the form of soil creep and, to a lesser extent, hill wash, supplies material to the streams and rivers which transport it to the sea. Under these conditions fluvial agencies are the dominant denudational process; frost-action is only very limited, partly because of the presence of a protective cover of vegetation.

Since Pliocene times the Wealden District has undergone intermittent isostatic uplift which has raised the margins of the area by some 600 ft relative to sea-level. Furthermore, during the Pleistocene glaciation, eustatic changes in sea-level also occurred. The net result of these two effects has been for the rate of erosion of the area, which varies in sympathy with the gradient of the river profiles, to be continually rapid, but with occasional periods of still-stand at times of temporary higher sea-level. Thus, although the Wealden uplift is a maturely dissected structure many of the land forms and much of the drainage within it still have a youthful aspect.

The most impressive feature of the scenery of our area is the manner in which the domal form of the Wealden uplift has been picked out by erosion. The uplift is roughly elliptical in plan, but the English Channel, breaching the dome near its eastern end has separated the Bas Boulonnais (the contination of the Weald in northern France) from the remainder of the structure. Five distinct regions can be recognized within the area, each following the trend of the main fold and each characterized by its own distinctive geological and topographical features. The central part of the Weald is composed of sandstones and clays of the Hastings Beds and forms an area of deeply dissected high ground rising in places to over 700 ft O.D.; this is surrounded by a broad zone of lower-lying land occupied by the outcrop of the soft shales of the Weald Clay. This in turn is surrounded by the Lower Greensand escarpment (Plate II) which reaches nearly 1,000 ft O.D. in the Leith Hill district of Surrey and includes the highest parts of the Weald. Along its northern outcrop, in Kent and Surrey, the Lower Greensand is thickly developed and, except near Guildford, contains either resistant cherts or sandy limestone (Fig. 6) in its lower part; in contrast, much of the southern outcrop is comprised of less resistant lithologies and further, thins eastwards from west Sussex almost to nothing in east Sussex. Consequently the Lower Greensand escarpment is well developed on the northern and western flanks but in the south it becomes less prominent eastwards, eventually disappearing north of Lewes. The Chalk Downs encircle the Lower Greensand hills, from which they are separated by a narrow belt of low-lying ground marked by the outcrop of the soft Folkestone Beds and the Gault. In contrast to that of the Lower Greensand the Chalk escarpment is remarkably constant in height throughout its length, a feature which reflects the lithological uniformity of the Chalk.

Within the generalized outline described above smaller features occur in response to facies variations within the major divisions; folds and lines of faulting also find topographical expression. This reflection of both major and minor features is exemplified by the drainage pattern of the area, which is essentially radial in concordance with the overall form of the uplift but which has subsequently been greatly modified by streams eroding back along the strike of the softer formations. In detail, folding, faulting, jointing and lithological variations all play an important part in governing the course of the drainage.

Although of negligible importance as denudational features, landslipping and cambering occur frequently in the Weald, often in similar geological settings.

*Landslips*

Landslips, as distinct from mudflows, usually occur where massive strata such as sandstones or limestones overlie less competent shales or clays; they are comparatively common along some of the escarpments and along the coast of our area. Movement normally occurs along rotational slip planes so that the back part of the slipped mass moves vertically downwards leaving a steep backface, whilst the front, or toe, is raised up by a proportionately lesser amount. Water acts as a lubricant to the slip planes and slips usually occur during or soon after periods of wet weather. Landslips are common along the Lower Greensand scarp-slope where the Hythe Beds overlie the Atherfield and Weald Clays and in places along the Chalk escarpments where the Chalk and the Gault are involved. They are best observed however along the coast, for the steeply dipping disturbed beds in the toe of the slips can usually be examined in the foreshore at low tides. Good examples occur on the Eastbourne side of Beachy Head and at Folkestone Warren, between Folkestone and Dover, where movement has taken place along slip planes in the Gault; at Ecclesbourne Glen, near Hastings, and at Hythe and Sandgate movement occurs on the Fairlight Clays and the Weald Clay respectively.

The best documented landslip in our area is that of Folkestone Warren; here Chalk cliffs up to 400 ft high overlie the Gault. Twelve major slips were recorded between 1765 and 1937, one of the most important of these being in 1915 when the whole of the Warren was disturbed and the Folkestone to Dover railway, which runs across the landslip, was laterally displaced by up to 55 yd (Plate XB).

Movement occurs along slip planes which go down to the base of the Gault, horizontal shearing just above the junction with the Folkestone Beds being lubricated by water from the latter. Immediately after the 1915 slip a chain of islands, composed of Gault, over half a mile long and up to 30 ft high at low tide, were formed on the foreshore in the toe of the slip and large quantities of Chalk fell from the backface. Subsequent marine erosion of the Gault islands was rapid and the removal of this weight from the toe made the slip unstable again so that further movement could take place. The other coastal examples mentioned above probably have a similar mechanism of regeneration. In recent years the construction of large concrete rafts on the foreshore to add weight to the toe and of drainage adits in the slipped mass have considerably reduced the possibility of further movement.

Mudflows occur in thick clays or weathered shales which have become plastic through saturation by water; the best examples are along the London Clay cliffs of the north Kent coast and in the Isle of Sheppey; the Gault at Folkestone and the Fairlight Clays at Fairlight Glen, near Hastings, also provide minor examples.

*Cambering*

Cambering is a type of structure best developed where gently dipping strata such as sandstone or limestone overlie thick clays. The harder beds are curved over the crests of escarpments and lowered towards valleys. This gentle arching is accompanied by the development of fissures, known as gulls, aligned parallel to the contours of the cambered slope, and by valley-ward tilting of the strata between the gulls, known as dip-and-fault structure. Flow of clay from beneath the cambered slopes to the valley bottom, and its removal by stream erosion, appears to have been an essential part of the cambering process. Sharp anticlinal structures thus produced are known as valley-bulges. Cambering and valley-bulging may well have been largely brought about under conditions of perennially frozen ground during glacial periods in the Pleistocene.

The strata around Maidstone, particularly the Hythe Beds in the Medway valley and on the escarpment from Mereworth in the west to Ulcombe in

(A.7876)

A. The Medway Gap in the North Downs, near Wouldham, Kent

B. The Chalk Cliffs of the Seven Sisters, from Seaford Head, Sussex

(*For full explanation see p. xi*)

(A.9751)

(Photo: Committee for Aerial Photography, University of Cambridge

A. Shingle Ridges on Dungeness

B. Degraded Sea Cliff below the Strand Gate, Winchelsea, Sussex

(*For full explanation see p. xii*)

(A.974

the east, show extraordinary fissures, filled with brickearth and other drift deposits. One has been recorded as being as much as 50 yd wide and a quarter of a mile long, and others as extending to a depth of more than 80 ft. They are known to quarrymen of the district as ' wents.' In 1862 W. H. Bensted, a quarry-owner and amateur geologist, gave a graphic description of the disturbed beds, but his explanation that the fissures were channels carved by great torrents of water, and which became filled with sediment as the flood subsided, did not find acceptance; after C. Le Neve Foster and W. Topley in 1865 described them simply as large solution-pipes, interest in the structures lapsed.

More recent work in the Maidstone area has shown that the Hythe Beds are cambered and that the ' wents ' of the area are gulls. Cambering on the Hythe Beds escarpments and in the Medway valley is illustrated in Fig. 16. Foster and Topley noted one case in which a gull extended through the entire thickness of Hythe Beds down to the underlying Atherfield Clay, and such complete penetration may be not uncommon. It is suggested by quarries such as that at Tovil (Fig. 16), where the Hythe Beds, which cannot be much more than 100 ft thick, are intersected by gulls 20 yd wide and seen to extend to a depth of 30 ft with no sign of their walls coming together. Cambering is also developed on the Hythe Beds escarpment near Hythe in Kent, and near Grayswood and on the east side of Black Down at the western end of the Weald.

In the Hastings Beds outcrop cambering occurs on a small scale where the massive sandstone of the Lower Tunbridge Wells Sand has slipped over the Wadhurst Clay: joint-widening in the sandstone is common but only a minor feature. Where the surrounding topographical relief is high, complementary valley-bulging is visible in the steeply dipping and sharply folded stream outcrops of the Wadhurst Clay; the Purbeck Beds, the Grinstead Clay and the Weald Clay (Plate XA) are similarly affected in valley floors.

## Inland Scenery

The Wealden District contains a number of striking and well-known pieces of scenery; some of these, together with the geological reasons underlying their formation, are described below.

### *The Leith Hill District*

This district includes the four well-known hills of Leith Hill, Holmbury Hill, Coneyhurst Hill (Pitch Hill) and Winterfold Heath, and forms the highest part of the Lower Greensand outcrop of the Weald, the top of Leith Hill being 965 ft above sea-level (Plate II); it is also characterized by some of the most picturesque scenery of the area.

The geology is simple (Fig. 17). The Leith Hill range is in effect the escarpment of the Hythe Beds. Chert beds occupy the topmost part of the hill and overlie sandy beds, which again overlie the Atherfield Clay, resting on Weald Clay. The chert beds are very resistant to erosion and protect the underlying sands and clay, which without protection are easily denuded.

The profile of the scarp-slope consists of two parts, the upper very steep, and the lower more gently inclined, the change in slope taking place at the junction of sandy beds with clay. A line of springs runs round the hills at this junction, and forms a very striking marshy belt, a few yards wide, traceable for a number of miles along the face of the escarpment. After a wet season this belt is impassable except at a few spots. The spring line is formed by water which percolates through the sand, but is thrown out on reaching the impervious clay. It has a pronounced effect on topography, since it rapidly removes sand from the base of the Hythe Beds and causes collapse of the rocks above, thereby leaving in places vertical cliffs up to 30 ft or more in height. The dip-slopes of the Leith Hill range are very gentle and almost coincide with the northerly dip of the beds. Because of the porous nature of the rocks water drains through rapidly, the soil is generally very dry and the country is either heathland or coniferous woodland; in the valleys which separate the hills, however, the top of the water table is either just above or just below the surface, and the land is more fertile.

Other parts of the Lower Greensand escarpment, such as Ide Hill and Brasted Hill, have origins similar to that of Leith Hill.

*St. Martha's Hill*

St. Martha's Hill, near Guildford, is the chief feature of the view seen from Newlands Corner. Composed of Lower Greensand, at first glance it resembles Leith Hill, but it has a somewhat different origin. The highest part consists of Folkestone Beds, and the apparent anomaly of soft, unconsolidated sand forming a high hill is thereby presented. The explanation is to be found in the presence of masses of ferruginous sandstone or ' carstone ' having a ' honeycomb ' structure, which are irregularly dispersed through the Folkestone Beds in such a way that this carstone simulates a thick, hard bed which has resisted erosion and now forms the top of the hill. The beds are steeply inclined and a bed of limestone in the Bargate Beds below forms a subsidiary scarp slightly southward of the Folkestone Beds scarp. But for the presence of the carstone, this limestone would probably form the top of a hill, which would be considerably lower than the present one.

*The Devil's Punchbowl, Hindhead*

The Devil's Punchbowl is one of the best known valleys in Surrey. A stream flowing northwards has cut a valley through the Hythe Beds down to the Atherfield Clay, and springs at the base of the Hythe Beds produce steep slopes above them, as at Leith Hill. A little to the north the dip steepens, and as the Atherfield Clay is carried underground, so the spring line disappears. By the undermining action of the springs the valley-head has tended to become larger and wider than the remainder of the valley, producing the ' Punchbowl.'

*The Escarpments and Coombes of the North and South Downs*

The striking escarpments of both the North and South Downs are similar in origin to the Lower Greensand escarpment. The comparatively hard Chalk (together with the Upper Greensand where present) is everywhere underlain by the soft Gault clay. Sub-aerial denudation, having cut down to these soft beds, gradually undermines the harder bed, thereby producing a steep slope. The escarpment of the North Downs is continually moving northward, and that of the South Downs is receding southward.

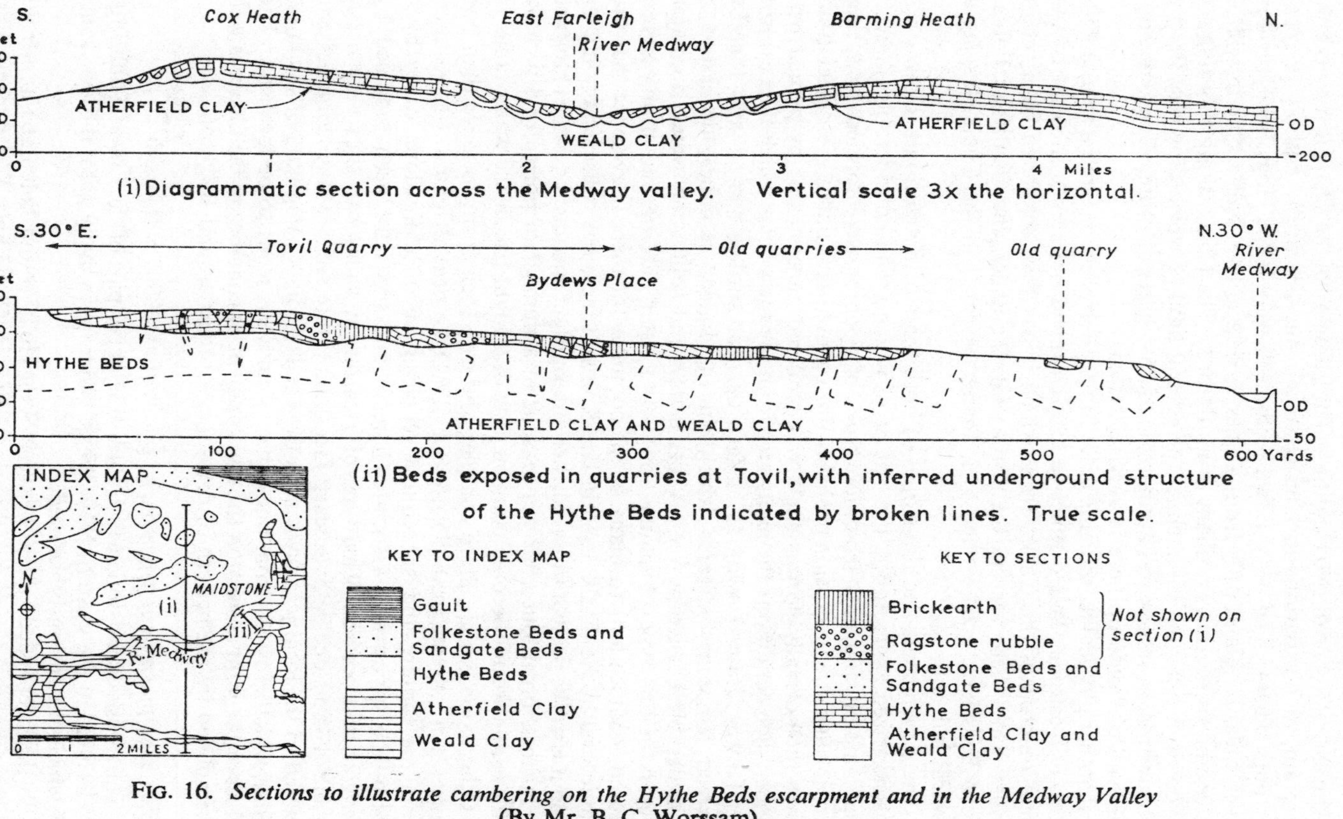


FIG. 16. *Sections to illustrate cambering on the Hythe Beds escarpment and in the Medway Valley*
(By Mr. B. C. Worssam)

Throughout the area the Chalk escarpments maintain a great similarity in form, except in one or two localities. The lithology of the Chalk is remarkably constant, and variations in land form are due practically entirely to local tectonic causes. The best-known tectonic feature is the Hogs Back, a ridge seven miles long and only from a quarter of a mile to half a mile in width, extending from near Farnham to Guildford. The Chalk along this ridge is involved in a faulted monocline, the central limb of which dips very steeply northwards, in some cases at an angle of 55 degrees or more. Consequently, the width of outcrop here is very restricted.

Another physical feature due to faulting is Belvedere or Summerhouse Hill, near Folkestone. This distinctive Chalk-capped hill stands in front of the main outcrop of the Chalk, from which it has been separated by a set of faults. On all sides except the north-west, the underlying Gault and Folkestone Beds have been eroded to a greater extent than the Chalk, leaving a conical hill.

The escarpments and dip-slopes of both the North and South Downs are characterized by coombes, the origins of which are of considerable interest. The simplest and most common types of coombe were formed by spring sapping and stream erosion probably during and immediately after glaciation, when the normally porous chalk was rendered impermeable by permafrost. Under such conditions the meltwater from the snow fields which then capped the Downs drained away as surface or near surface run-off and thereby formed temporary streams which, in the longer coombes, developed a considerable erosive power. [Frost action and solifluxion were also major factors in this type of denudation]. At a later date normal spring action caused modifications to many of the coombes for there is evidence that the water level in the Chalk, even in late Roman times, was considerably higher than it is at the present time; further, intermittent streams, known as bournes or lavants, break out after wet seasons in a number of normally dry chalk valleys and would become permanent with a slight rise in the water table.

Other coombes are more complex and owe their form to more than one cause. An extreme example, the Devil's Dyke near Brighton, has resulted from the capture and subsequent rejuvenation of a dip-slope valley by a scarp-face spring and associated stream and has later been modified by periglacial processes. This type of escarpment valley can thus only occur where a dip-slope and a scarp-face valley intersect. Many coombes are related to the local joint system in the Chalk; joints being lines of weakness along which erosion, from one cause or another, tends to be localized. The effect of the joint system on the development of coombes in the Chalk is well exemplified by the pattern of dry valley systems around Brighton.

*West Hoathly Rocks, High Rocks etc.*

The massive sandstone which forms the upper part of the Lower Tunbridge Wells Sand in the western High Weald outcrops in many natural crags, some of which are curiously isolated.

In the steep-sided valleys between West Hoathly and Balcombe numerous outcrops occur, the most imposing being in Chiddingly Wood near West Hoathly, where well-jointed sandstone is slightly cambered (p. 69) so that large rectangular blocks have become separated from the main outcrop by

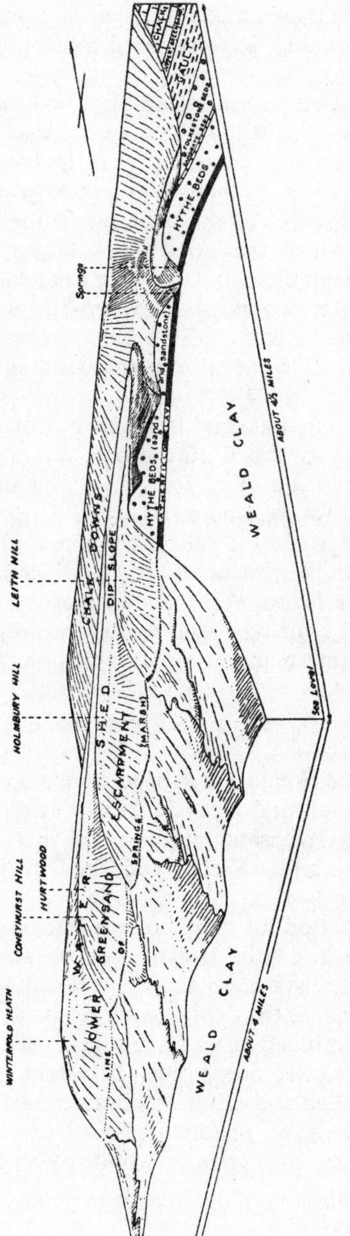


FIG. 17. *Block-diagram to show the relationship of scenery to geology in the Leith Hill district of Surrey*

narrow vertical chasms up to 35 ft deep. Along much of the outcrop the rock wall has been undercut by water seepage at an horizon where the sandstone is slightly more silty and consequently less porous. In one occurrence, Great-upon-Little, the result of undercutting on a mass, isolated from the main outcrop by joint-widening, has produced a block which overhangs on all sides.

Harrison's Rocks near Groombridge and High Rocks and Eridge Rocks near Tunbridge Wells also frequently show spectacular joint-widening and undercutting. This latter appears to result from the erosive effects of wind-blown sand rather than from a change in lithology or undermining by seepages. Around Tunbridge Wells the same sandstone has been weathered into isolated blocks, of which the Toad Rock (Plate IIIA), on Rusthall Common, is an extreme example. Undercutting has taken place along a less resistant layer lying between two massive beds, partly by water seepage and partly by wind action: the isolation of the block from the main outcrop is probably due to removal of some of the surrounding stone for building purposes.

Mantell, comparing their likeness to that of much coastal scenery, attributed the form of the sandrock outcrops to marine erosion and wrote "..... That romantic spot, the *High Rocks* ..... is manifestly an ancient shore—a line of cliffs that for ages bore the brunt of the waves ....." We now know that the outcrops and the valleys containing them were formed by normal subaerial denudational processes and that their erosion is continuing at the present day. Percolating water is the main erosive agent with cambering and frost action producing many of the minor features present. In recent years re-afforestation around many of the outcrops has eliminated the effect of wind action.

*Sunken Roads*

The sunken roads of the Weald are a good example of the action of man as a geological agent. Roads and farm tracks of this type are common over the whole of the Lower Greensand outcrop and in some localities on the outcrops of the Lower Tunbridge Wells Sand, the Upper Greensand and the Chalk.

All stages in their formation may still be seen, ranging from simple tracks to cuttings 20 ft or more in depth. Initially the surface vegetation is killed along a track which is in constant use and the soft soil and subsoil layers are soon broken up by the traffic, the debris being removed by rainwater. Over a period of centuries continued use of the track, particularly by wheeled vehicles, gradually widens and deepens it. In recent years many of these roadways have been metalled and artificially drained so that downcutting has been arrested; the advent of pneumatic tyres has reduced erosion in unmetalled lanes where the iron rims of wooden wheels previously caused much damage.

*River Development and Chalk Gaps*

A small part of the drainage system of the Weald is still related to streams which were initiated during early Pleistocene times. The best examples of this are the deep valleys or gaps in the North and South Downs which cut directly across the major geological structures and which are obviously a much earlier feature than the coombes and dry valleys whose form they have in many cases controlled. With the exception of the Rivers Ashburn, Brede and Rother all the Wealden rivers flow through a Chalk gap for part of their course. Superficially these gaps are very similar to one another, but in detail each has its own individual features, dependent upon differences in their geological situation. As examples of these differences, the gaps of the Darent, the Mole, the Arun and the Ouse are compared below.

*The Darent gap* is a steep-sided, rather narrow valley, with low-lying ground covered with a large area of gravel just above river level at its entrance. This gravel, spread over the Gault and Folkestone Beds, indicates that at a comparatively recent period in the history of the river water was held up behind the Chalk escarpment, the upper part of the Darent valley being then graded to the level of the comparatively hard Chalk but not to sea-level. In this upper part considerably more lateral cutting by the river occurred than where the river crosses the Chalk.

*The Mole valley* at Dorking has little valley gravel or alluvium within that part running through the Chalk. Its chief features are its striking river cliffs, its narrowness compared with other Chalk gaps of equal importance and the habit of the River Mole of disappearing underground along part of its course during dry weather: this last feature explains the other two. The river disappears through swallow-holes, which in part owe their existence to a ' step ' in the thalweg of the river, which occurs about midway through the gap. This step allows the water table to fall to just below the surface level when the river is low, and swallow holes result. The positions of the known swallow holes are shown in Fig. 18.

It is possible that conditions favourable to the formation of swallow holes have existed in the Mole gap for a very long period of time, and that in the upper part of the gap erosion has proceeded downward partly by the solvent action of water on chalk. It is noteworthy that a ' fossil ' swallow hole, now filled with sand, has been observed beneath terraced river gravel. The special scenery of the Mole gap may therefore be associated with the presence of swallow holes.

*The Arun gap* has a great spread of alluvium bounded by steep river cliffs in its upper part. The Gault outcrop here forms a 'V' downstream, but the whole area is affected by a series of minor east-to-west folds, and one of these rapidly takes the base of the Chalk to below river level about a mile within the gap. As a result of this structure, the Arun has cut sideways more rapidly where soft beds are at stream level than it has where hard chalk constitutes its bed, and has thereby carved a wide, funnel-shaped entrance to the Arun gap.

*The River Ouse* at Lewes has a wide expanse of alluvium with two small eminences protruding through it in the middle of its Chalk gap. This is explained by the presence of a sharp fold which brings Gault to the surface and, as in the case of the Arun, the river has widened its valley over the outcrop of this soft bed more rapidly than over the outcrop of the harder Chalk, but in the Ouse valley the alluvium is within the gap instead of at the entrance.

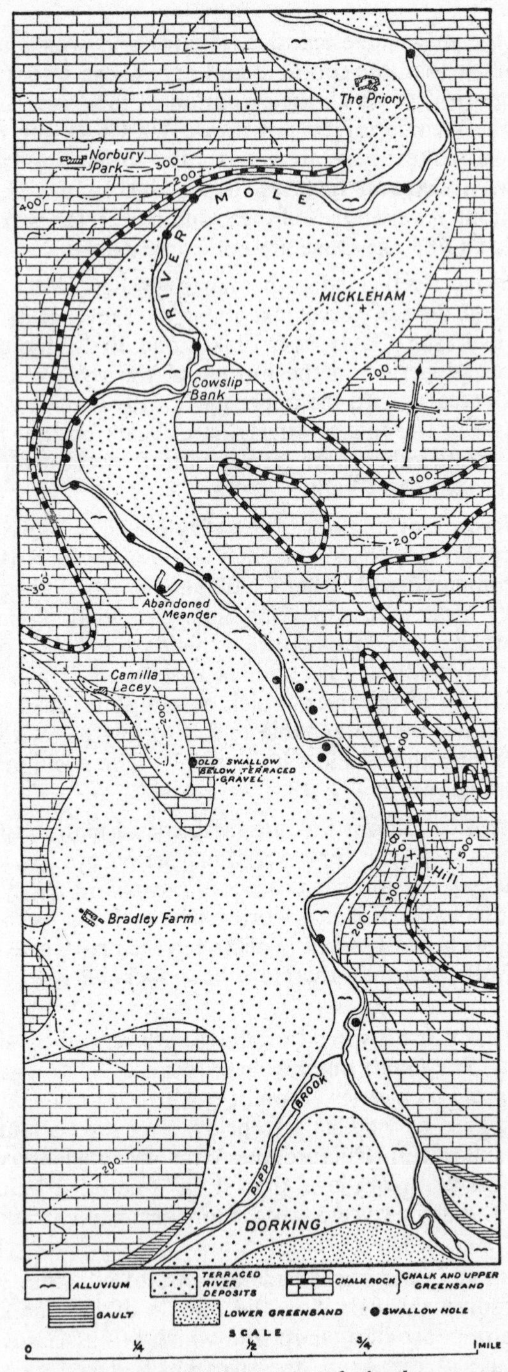


FIG. 18. *Sketch-map showing the positions of the known swallow-holes in the valley of the River Mole north of Dorking, Surrey*
(From 'Geology of the country around Reigate and Dorking,' *Mem. Geol. Surv.*, 1933)

Among the numerous modifications which have been made to the original radial drainage system of our area, river capture has been a common occurrence, one of the best examples being the capture of the headwaters of the River Blackwater by those of the River Wey (Fig. 19). H. Bury showed that the Wey first captured two tributaries of the Blackwater (second stage) before capturing the main head waters (final stage). As a result, the present River Wey, near Godalming, flows in a deep gorge-like valley, while the Blackwater is a ' misfit,' flowing in a valley much too large for so small a stream. The branch of the River Wey flowing through Bramley also has a complicated history; its headwaters on the Weald Clay above Dunsfold were captured by the River Arun at some time after the main stream of the Wey had captured the head of the Blackwater.

## Coastal Scenery

The form of the present day coast of the Weald is dependent upon a number of interrelated factors, the two most important being the variations in hardness of the rocks involved and the rise in sea-level which has occurred since Neolithic times. It has previously been noted that in our area the more resistant beds tend to stand out as hills and the softer to form lower-lying ground and this is reflected in the coastal scenery. Cliffs occur where the sea is cutting into hills, and indentations occur where valleys are present; consequently, in general, cliffs occur where the hard strata of the Ashdown Sand, the Lower Greensand and the Chalk meet the sea, but are absent along the shores formed by the Wadhurst Clay, the Weald Clay and Drift deposits.

Since the end of the Pleistocene period the mean sea-level relative to the land has risen approximately 100 ft in our area, causing the coastline to become drowned and subsequently modified by the higher sea-level. Initially the river valleys were ria-like and the headlands rounded and smooth. Rapid sedimentation in valleys and in shallow bays has since formed alluvial flats or ' levels ' and the enhanced erosive power of the sea has cut back the headlands to form prominent lines of cliffs.

Longshore drift also plays an important part in controlling the shape of the coastline. Along the South Coast material moves from west to east under the action of the dominant south-westerly winds and has diverted to the east the mouths of all the major rivers. Large accumulations of shingle, mostly flint pebbles, tend to collect in the bays formed by the softer strata, thus protecting them from further erosion. Langney Point in Pevensey Bay, and Dungeness are notable examples.

Some of the more important features of the coastline of the Wealden District are described below.

### *Sandstone and Clay Cliffs*

The cliffs between Hastings and Pett Level are composed of Ashdown Sand which is flexed into a shallow, faulted anticline, the Fairlight Anticline. The upper part of the formation, consisting predominantly of massive, well jointed sandstones, forms vertical cliffs at Hastings and at Pett Level, the former up to 300 ft high. In the centre of the anticline the more argillaceous lower part of the formation consists of alternating massive sandstones and shales, the Fairlight Clays, which give rise to smaller cliffs obscured by large

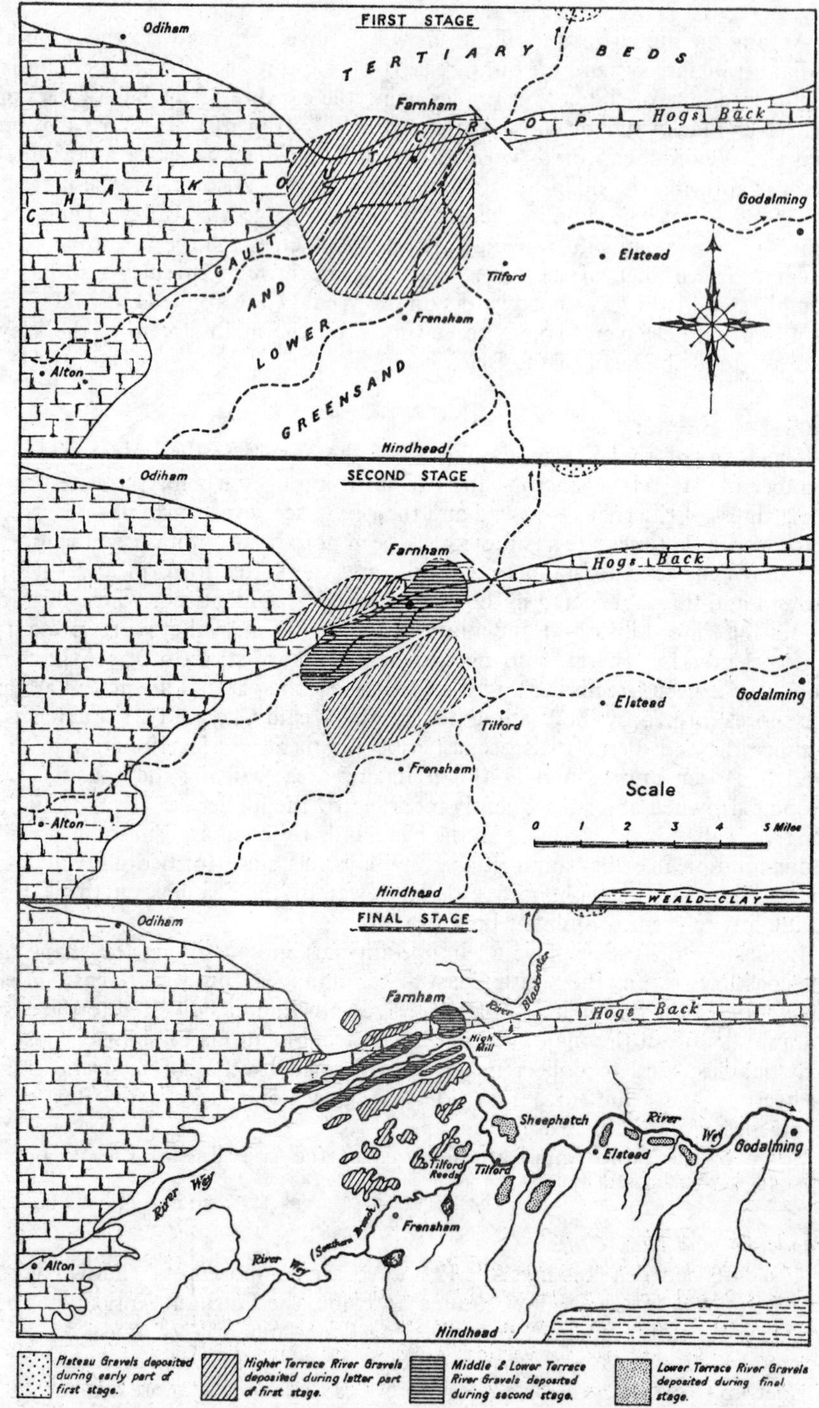


FIG. 19. *Diagrams showing stages of river capture in the neighbourhood of Farnham, Surrey*

mudflows. Near Ecclesbourne Glen rotational landslip along planes in the Fairlight Clays has produced low cliffs in front of the main cliff line.

At this locality marine erosion is more rapid than sub-aerial erosion so that the streams in Ecclesbourne and Fairlight Glens have been unable to grade their valleys to sea-level in pace with the retreat of the cliffs and are now perched in hanging valleys.

At Copt Point, near Folkestone, vertical cliffs of Folkestone Beds are overlain by the Gault; this latter frequently slips, leaving funnel-shaped hollows in the cliffs (Plate IXB).

Cliffs of London Clay, up to 150 ft high, occur between Whitstable and Reculver and along the northern side of the Isle of Sheppey. Mudflows and landslips obscure much of the section and erosion, both by the sea and by land water, is rapid.

*Chalk Cliffs*

The intersection of both the South and North Downs with the sea gives rise to imposing chalk cliffs between Brighton and Eastbourne and between Folkestone and the Isle of Thanet respectively.

Between Brighton and Beachy Head the coastline approximately follows the strike of the Chalk and forms an almost continuous line of cliffs, culminating in Beachy Head 525 ft high. This section of coast is exposed to south-westerly gales and the Chalk here is homogenous and has few open joints. Consequently the cliffs are cleanly cut and are nearly vertical. A well developed wave cut platform occurs at the foot of the cliffs and shows the jointing in plan. Numerous dry valleys, which run down the dip-slopes of the Chalk, have been cut back by marine erosion and can now be seen in transverse cross section in the cliffs. The best examples of these are the small valleys in the coast section known as the Seven Sisters (Plate XIIB) east of the outfall of the River Cuckmere.

In Kent the chalk cliffs are separated into two sections by a syncline containing Eocene beds, south of the Isle of Thanet. Between Folkestone and Deal the cliffs are very similar to those near Eastbourne, but in the Isle of Thanet, where the Chalk is affected by numerous small fracture planes and joints, the cliffs are lower and ' sea stacks ' are numerous. Various stages in the development of sea stacks can be seen around the coastline of the Isle of Thanet. Marine erosion along planes of weakness in the Chalk produces irregular shaped promontories which are eventually breached by the sea forming natural arches (Front Cover) which in time collapse to give isolated stacks.

*Alluvial Flats or ' Levels '*

Both Pevensey Levels and Romney Marsh, the most extensive alluvial flats in our area, were initially shallow bays which have since silted up and been artificially drained behind a protective fringe of shingle. Several small islands in the original bay at Pevensey now stand out above the levels as low hills. Other alluvial flats occur around Arundel and Lewes, in the Wantsum Strait in north-east Kent and in the Medway and Swale estuaries around the Isle of Sheppey. All these occurrences are sited in the lower reaches or at the outfall of drowned valleys which contain river and estuarine deposits up to 100 ft thick.

At the present-day salt marshes fringe much of the Medway and Swale estuaries and have occupied all the above mentioned areas within historic times. In their lower reaches many of the Wealden rivers now meander extensively across these alluvial flats: the Ouse and the Cuckmere (Plate XI B) are particularly good examples of this.

*Dungeness and Romney Marsh*

The promontory of Dungeness is the largest shingle structure in Britain and is made up of a complex series of shingle ridges, or fulls, many of which lie at high angles to the present coastline (Plate XIII A). Romney Marsh and the adjacent Walland and Denge Marshes are reclaimed areas formed behind the protective barrier of fulls, although at the present time a sea wall protects the marshland adjacent to Dymchurch Bay where the shingle has been removed by erosion. The geological and archaeological histories of the Marshes are closely linked and have been the subject of several investigations, and some controversy; the account by W. V. Lewis (1932) being the most comprehensive.

Early writers suggested that the shingle ridges were thrown up by the meeting of the tides of the North Sea and the English Channel. F. P. Gulliver, in 1897, first put forward the theory of a migrating cuspate foreland which forms the basis of most modern explanations.

At the end of the Neolithic period, some 3000 to 4000 years ago, the area between Fairlight Head and Hythe was occupied by a large shallow, sandy bay, into which the estuaries of the Rivers Rother, Tillingham and Brede discharged. All evidence of the limits of this bay in the region of the Fairlight and Hythe headlands has been removed by subsequent coastal erosion, but where this old coastline has been protected by later deposits the degraded remains of an ancient sea cliff are preserved as a steep feature which is still almost continuous between Winchelsea (Plate XIII B) and Hythe. At the present time the supply of shingle to the Ness, is composed mostly of flints derived from the Chalk cliffs of Sussex which lie to the west. It is probable therefore that at first, spits formed at Fairlight Head, which would have extended farther seaward at that time, and ran north-eastwards into the bay towards the Brede estuary (Fig. 20, line 1) in much the same manner as the present Camber ridges. Further extensions to these spits (line 2) aided by a fall in sea-level relative to the land surface, eventually formed a complete bay bar (line 3) behind which estuarine deposits from the three rivers rapidly accumulated until the bay became first a salting, then a marsh and finally was afforested. At this last stage the mean sea level was about 25 ft lower than at the present day and the area was probably drained by an estuary breaching the shingle near the present New Romney. A subsequent return of the sea to its original level drowned the forests, which can be traced at the present day as a widespread peat horizon, and the shoreline returned to its earliest position at the foot of the old cliff line, leaving only the shingle bar above water. Behind the shingle, deposition of estuarine sands and muds continued, burying the Forest Bed.

Rapid erosion of Fairlight Head, enhanced by the higher sea-level, caused a slight bend to form in the bay bar (line 4). It is probable that an estuary of the Brede and Tillingham, running out through the bar near Winchelsea,

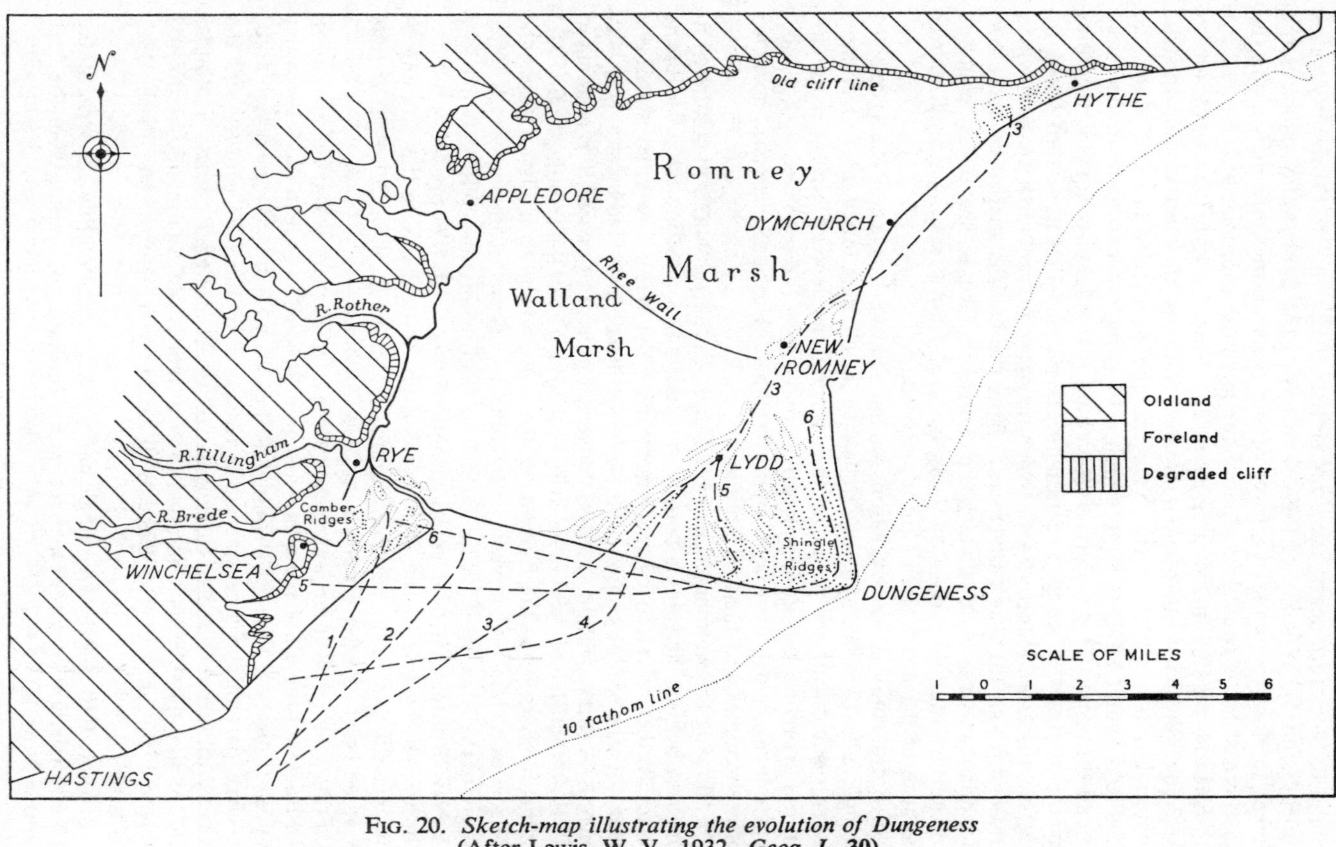


FIG. 20. *Sketch-map illustrating the evolution of Dungeness*
(After Lewis, W. V. 1932. *Geog. J.*, 30)

accentuated this bend by starving the shore farther east of shingle and thus causing it to retreat more rapidly under wave action so that it tended to swing round to face more nearly the dominant southerly and south-westerly waves (lines 5 and 6). A study of the conditions at the point today indicates the forces tending to mould the form of the Ness. Longshore drift along the southern shore is caused by the oblique angle of approach of the prevalent up-Channel waves. In swinging round the Ness, however, the waves are so weakened that in spite of their greater obliquity they are unable to drift material northward from the Ness as rapidly as they bring it along the southern shore, so that large supplies of shingle accumulate immediately round the point. This material is then built into ridges overlapping the point by the south-west waves and into ridges parallel to the eastern shore by east-north-easterly storm waves which originate in the North Sea and which travel through the Strait of Dover. Thus the Ness is shaped by these two dominant wave directions which the two shores face, its sharpness being due to the fact that no large waves can reach it from a south-easterly quarter because of the proximity of the French coast.

From a study of the variations in the relative heights of the groups of shingle fulls it has been possible to deduce the changes in sea-level which have taken place during the period of their formation, since each ridge represents an old shoreline and its height will be related to the sea-level at that time. These levels can in turn be related to archaeological and historical accounts of the marshes and their reclamation.

Following the submergence of the Forest Bed, sedimentation continued in the area behind the shingle until it was once again a salting estuary with the River Rother, diverted by the migration of the Ness, now entering the sea near Winchelsea in conjunction with the Brede and Tillingham (Fig. 20, line 5). A further fall in sea-level converted much of the area into marshland so that the Belgae, a Gallic tribe occupying part of southern England immediately prior to the Roman occupation, and the Romans, to whom the Belgae were later subservient, were able to occupy Romney Marsh. The origin of the Rhee Wall, a channel 80 ft to 100 ft wide running from Appledore to New Romney, is problematical and complex. It was probably initially constructed by one of the above groups either to facilitate the draining of the marshlands or to carry additional water from the Rother to a port situated on its former estuary near New Romney.

Following the Roman withdrawal from Britain there was a further rise in sea-level, and much of the area was again flooded so that in the 9th century a fleet of piratical Danes was able to sail past Lydd and into the marshlands. A large part of the area was again reclaimed in the 13th century and the Rhee Wall was repaired to carry water to a port at New Romney. Reclamation of the marshlands continued intermittently and was mainly completed by the 17th century; the Rhee Wall probably fell into disuse in the 16th century.

Erosion of the protective shingle barrier in Dymchurch Bay has necessitated the construction of a series of sea walls, the first one dating from the 15th century, to take its place.

# 9. Economic Geology

*Water Supply*

Although the water supplies for a few communities are obtained by impounding surface streams or by direct abstraction from rivers, the majority of the domestic and industrial water requirements of the Wealden District are met by underground works constructed in water-bearing rocks, termed aquifers. This dependence upon ground water is emphasised by the absence of sufficiently extensive impermeable catchment areas which would be suitable for the development of large impounding schemes. The geological history of the district has determined the distribution of the aquifers, and accordingly the availability of water supplies in a particular locality is closely associated with the local geology. Water resources have been fully exploited in some of the more densely populated districts and are augmented by supplies from less developed areas.

Of the rocks in the Wealden District which contain and yield reliable supplies of good quality water, the Chalk is the most prolific. The Lower Greensand is next in order of importance, whilst the sandy divisions of the Hastings Beds are utilized to a lesser extent. Although the clay formations in the area do not generally yield water, they exert great influence on the circulation and storage of ground water. Locally where no other sources of water are available, small supplies have been derived from Pleistocene and Recent deposits, as well as from thin sandy and calcareous beds within the clay formations.

The water content in aquifers is derived from rain which falls on their outcrops and percolates downwards to a saturated zone where it is temporarily stored before emerging as spring flow or seepages. The upper surface of the saturated zone is termed a ' water table ' and a spring or seepage is formed wherever this intersects the ground surface. The water table is subject to seasonal variations in level and intermittent springs or ' bournes,' such as the Lewes Winterbourne, may rise at sites reached by the water table at the crest of its fluctuations. In some districts such as the Isle of Sheppey, water is held under pressure in the aquifers by overlying clay formations. If a well is sunk through the clay, the water will rise under pressure and may result in the formation of an overflowing artesian well.

Saturated chalk yields water slowly but its capacity to transmit water is increased considerably by a network of fissures which traverses it, and which are fed by slow seepage from the main body of the rock. For a well to be successful, one or more water-filled fissure systems must be intersected. Fissures are of less significance in the sands of the Lower Greensand and Hastings Beds as water flows between the individual grains—the coarser grained Lower Greensand generally yielding more freely than the finer Hastings Beds.

Water supplies have been developed in the past, particularly in the Chalk of the Wealden area, by excavating adits from wells for considerable distances, as for example near Ramsgate where an adit system extends for four miles.

Recent practice, when large supplies are required, is to drill boreholes up to 36 inches in diameter and 400–500 ft deep, the depth depending principally upon geological factors. Yields in excess of 3 million gallons per day are obtained exceptionally from Chalk boreholes whilst supplies of 1 million gallons are relatively common. The Lower Greensand also yields copiously, 30 000 gallons per hour frequently being obtained, but the Hastings Beds are less prolific.

Ground water contains mineral salts dissolved from the soil and rocks through which it has passed. Of the various chemical characteristics thus imparted to the water, hardness is perhaps the property most commonly assessed. Chalk water is usually hard but can be softened naturally where the aquifer is overlain by Eocene strata. Ground water from the Lower Greensand at its outcrop is moderately hard while the Hastings Beds yield a soft water.

Abstraction of ground water from the Chalk at a few sites adjacent to the coastal outcrops in south Sussex and north Kent has lowered the level of fresh water to below sea level and sea-water has gained access to the wells.

### *Coal*

A bituminous and semi-anthracite coal with a high calorific value is mined in the Kent Coalfield. The Shakespeare Colliery at Dover was the first to be worked, the shaft being commenced in the year 1896; little coal was obtained, however, owing to water difficulties and the colliery was abandoned. Today four collieries, Tilmanstone, Betteshanger, Snowdown, and Chislet, are working.

Fourteen more or less persistent seams have been identified and these are generally numbered in descending order; Kent No. 1 is the highest seam workable; this is also known as the Beresford Seam at Tilmanstone and Snowdown. Seams being worked today (1964) are Kent No. 6, also known as the Millyard Seam at Snowdown and the 'F' Seam at Betteshanger and Kent No. 7 which is the No. 5 Seam of Chislet and the 'H' Seam of Betteshanger.

The deepest shaft is that of Tilmanstone, which reaches the No. 6 Seam at 3035 ft from ground surface, while the depths of the other shafts are:
Betteshanger, 2426 ft; Snowdown, 3020 ft; and Chislet, 1500 ft.

The output of coal in 1962 was about 1 456 800 tons saleable and an eventual output of between 1·5 and 2 million tons is regarded as possible. Reserves in this comparatively recently developed coalfield could be very substantial and give a life of well over a hundred years at this possible rate of output. But the geological conditions are variable and it is uncertain how much of the reserves will be economically workable.

### *Building Materials*

The Wealden area yields, in greater or less quantity, many types of building material. Building stone was formerly obtained from shelly limestones, '*Paludina*' limestone, in the Weald Clay and from sandstones in the Upper Greensand which were mined in considerable quantities near Reigate. Flints from the Chalk and, locally, chalk itself, have also been used. At the present time small quantities of building stone are obtained from the Ashdown Sand,

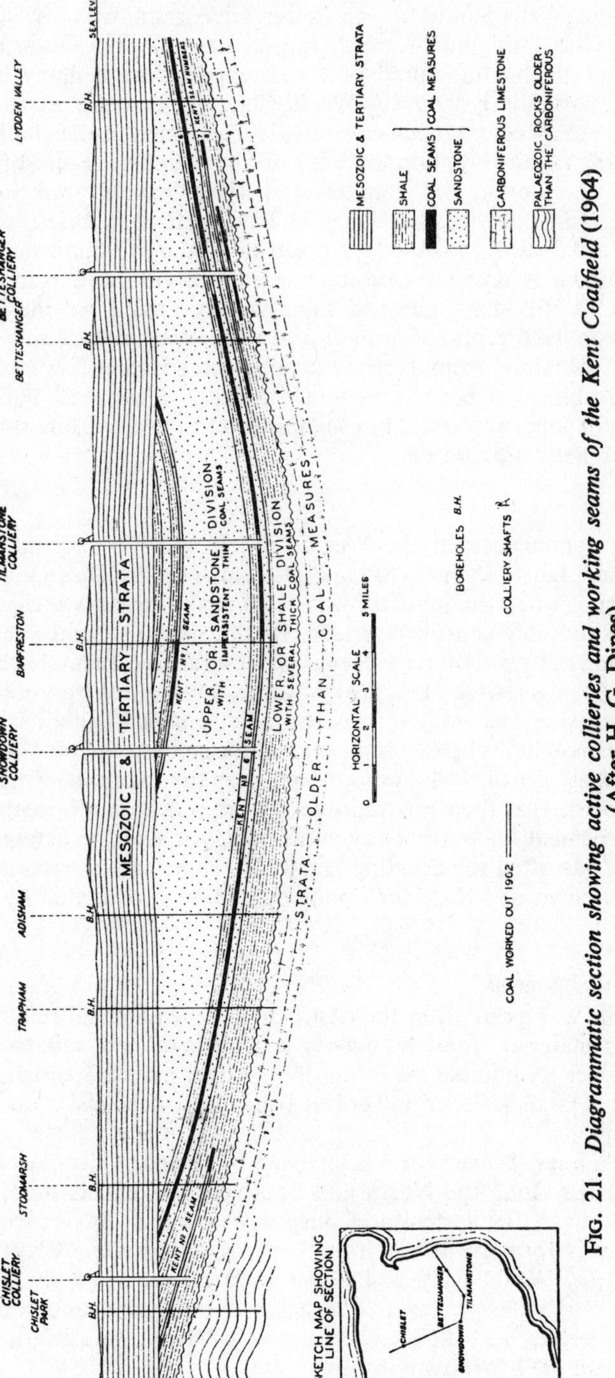


FIG. 21. *Diagrammatic section showing active collieries and working seams of the Kent Coalfield* (1964) (After H. G. Dines)

the Tunbridge Wells Sand and the Lower Greensand, which yields Bargate Stone near Godalming and Kentish Rag in Kent. Bricks of various grades and qualities are manufactured in large quantities from many of the clay formations, particularly from the Weald Clay. At Lewes, Portslade, Sittingbourne and near Rochester cement is made from a mixture of chalk and clay, the clay being Gault clay, London Clay or alluvial mud. Ballast for making concrete has been excavated from terraced River Gravels in the Stour Valley at Sturry and in the Medway Valley at Leybourne and Aylesford. Similar material is obtained from shingle deposits at Hythe and Sandwich, from the Camber ridges near Rye, the Crumbles near Eastbourne and from Dungeness (Plate XIII A). Building sand and silica sand are dug from the Folkestone Beds between Hythe and Farnham and near Washington and Hassocks. Sand is also obtained from Tertiary deposits near Canterbury and from the gravel and shingle deposits mentioned above. Plaster of Paris, Keen's Cement and similar materials are manufactured from gypsum, mined from the Purbeck Beds near Battle.

*Iron*

Smelting commenced in the Weald, which was formerly an important centre of the English iron industry, in pre-Roman times. During the 16th and 17th centuries, when the industry was at its peak, furnaces existed at about 70 localities, notably at Robertsbridge, Battle, Wadhurst and Sheffield Park in Sussex, and at Lamberhurst in Kent. The last furnace, that of Ashburnham, was closed down about 1811. Clay ironstone, a low grade iron ore consisting largely of siderite, was worked from sporadic beds in all subdivisions of the Wealden. Ferruginous ' pan ' of recent and Pleistocene age, was also utilized. While the sites of ironworks were placed near the outcrops of ironstone, it does not appear that their proximity to the ore was of first importance. The industry depended on water as a source of power and the configuration of the ground was often the deciding factor, works being sited where extensive reservoirs, known as ' Hammer Ponds,' could be constructed by damming valleys.

*Miscellaneous Products*

Roadstone was quarried in the past from all the harder formations in the Weald, but material from these beds is in general too soft to withstand modern traffic. A notable exception is provided by the Kentish Rag, now worked on a large scale. Flint gravel from Drift deposits is also used for road-making.

Chalk in a finely-broken form is quarried by means of mechanical scrapers at many places along the North and South Downs and is used, with and without additives, for agricultural purposes. Lime is obtained by burning chalk and was formerly made from Purbeck limestones. Clays from the Hastings Beds, Weald Clay and Gault were once extensively worked for ' Marl,' although they contain little calcium carbonate, and were applied indiscriminately to both light and heavy soils. The Chalk Marl, a genuine marl, was also used for this purpose.

Hearthstone, a soft friable sandstone used for whitening hearths and stone floors, was formerly mined from the Upper Greensand near Reigate.

Glass sand has been quarried at various localities from the Folkestone Beds, the Tunbridge Wells Sand and the Ashdown Sand, and in the Middle Ages glass manufacture was carried on at Chiddingfold and elsewhere.

Moulding sand is dug from the Folkestone Beds near Maidstone and from the Thanet Beds near Canterbury.

Fuller's earth is excavated from the Sandgate Beds at Nutfield.

In 1895 and 1896 natural gas was encountered in two boreholes at Heathfield which probably passed into the Upper Purbeck Beds. An analysis of the gas from the second borehole showed methane 91·9 per cent, hydrogen 7·2 per cent and nitrogen 0·9 per cent and this gas was used for many years to light the railway station. Further exploration in the area was unsuccessful and it was concluded that the gas-field was a small local pocket which had collected in an anticlinal crest. Small seepages of natural gas have also been recorded from boreholes in the Hastings Beds at Cuckfield and Battle.

Traces of oil have been noted near Eastbourne, and at Battle and Three Bridges but exploratory boreholes sited on several of the more promising anticlinal axes have so far failed to prove any reserves of commercial value.

# 10. Geological Survey Maps and Memoirs, and Short Bibliography of Other Works, Dealing with the Wealden District

## Maps

(*a*) **On the Scale of 4 miles to 1 in:** *Colour-printed* (*Out of print*)

Sheet 19. Bath, Guildford, Abingdon.
Sheet 20 with 24. London, Dover, Brighton.

(*b*) **On the Scale of 1 mile to 1 in:**

(i) *Old Series Sheets, hand-coloured* (*Out of print*)

Sheet 3. Canterbury, Margate.
,, 4. Folkestone and Rye.
,, 5.* Hastings, Eastbourne, Lewes.
,, 6.* Maidstone, Tunbridge Wells, East Grinstead.
,, 8.* Farnham, Guildford, Dorking.
,, 9.* Brighton, Chichester, Haslemere.

(ii) *New Series Sheets, colour-printed.*

Sheet 271. Dartford.
,, 272. Chatham.
,, 273. Faversham.
,, 274. Ramsgate.
,, 284. Basingstoke.
,, 285. Aldershot and Guildford.
,, 286. Reigate and Dorking.
,, 287. Sevenoaks.
,, 288. Maidstone.
,, 290. Dover.
,, 300. Alresford.
,, 316. Fareham.
,, 317. Chichester.
,, 318. Brighton.
,, 319. Lewes.
,, 320. Hastings.
,, 321. Dungeness. (*Out of print*)
,, 332. Bognor.
,, 333. Worthing. (*Out of print*)
,, 334. Eastbourne.

---

* Mostly replaced by New Series Sheets.

**(*c*) On the Scale of 6 in to 1 mile.**

The greater part of the area represented by New Series 1-in scale maps is also covered by maps on the 6-in scale. These are not published, but are in manuscript form, and may be consulted in the Geological Survey Library. Uncoloured photo-copies may be supplied on special order.

## Memoirs

**(*a*) General Memoirs:** (*Out of print*)

1864. DREW, F. The Geology of Folkestone and Rye, including Romney Marsh.
1872. WHITAKER, W. The Geology of the London Basin.
1875. TOPLEY, W. Geology of the Weald.
1899. WHITAKER, W. The Water Supply of Sussex.
1901–1904. JUKES-BROWNE, A. J. The Cretaceous Rocks of Britain. 3 vols. Appropriate sections deal with Wealden District.
1908. WHITAKER, W. Water Supply of Kent.
1911. LAMPLUGH, G. W. and KITCHIN, F. L. Mesozoic Rocks of Kent Coal Explorations.
1912. WHITAKER, W. Water Supply of Surrey.
1923. LAMPLUGH, G. W., KITCHIN, F. L. and PRINGLE, J. The Concealed Mesozoic Rocks in Kent.
1923. SPATH, L. F. "On the Ammonite Horizons of the Gault and Contiguous Deposits": Appendix II in *Summary of Progress for* 1922.
1928. EDMUNDS, F. H. Wells and Springs of Sussex.
1933. DINES, H. G., CROOKALL, R. and STUBBLEFIELD, C. J. Papers on the Kent Coalfield in *Summary of Progress for* 1932, Part II.
1962. CHALONER, W. G. Rhaeto-Liassic plants from the Henfield Borehole. *Bull. Geol. Surv. Gt. Brit.* **19,** 16–28.

**(*b*) New Series Sheet Memoirs:** (*Out of print unless otherwise stated*).

1897. REID, C. The Geology of the Country around Bognor (Sheet 332).
1898. REID, C. The Geology of the Country around Eastbourne (Sheet 334).
1903. REID, C. The Geology of the Country around Chichester (Sheet 317).
1924. WHITE, H. J. O. The Geology of the Country near Brighton and Worthing (Sheets 318 and 333).
1926. WHITE, H. J. O. The Geology of the Country near Lewes (Sheet 319).
1928. WHITE, H. J. O. The Geology of the Country near Hastings and Dungeness (Sheets 320 and 321).
1928. WHITE, H. J. O. The Geology of the Country near Ramsgate and Dover (Sheets 274 and 290).
1929. DINES, H. G. and EDMUNDS, F. H. The Geology of the Country around Aldershot and Guildford (Sheet 285).
1933. DINES, H. G. and EDMUNDS, F. H. The Geology of the Country around Reigate and Dorking (Sheet 286).
1954. DINES, H. G., HOLMES, S. C. A. and ROBBIE, J. A. The Geology of the Country around Chatham (Sheet 272) (*In print*). Price 21*s*.
1963. WORSSAM, B. C. Geology of the Country around Maidstone (Sheet 288) (*In print*). Price 25*s*.

## Short Bibliography of Other Works

ALLEN, P. 1954. Geology and Geography of the London-North Sea Uplands in Wealden times. *Geol. Mag.*, **91**, 498–508.

—— 1959. The Wealden environment: Anglo-Paris Basin. *Phil. Trans.*, Ser. B., **242**, No. 692, 283-346.

—— 1960. Geology of the Central Weald: The Hastings Beds. *Geol. Assoc. Guides*, No. 24.

—— 1962. The Hastings Beds Deltas: Recent Progress and Easter Field Meeting Report. *Proc. Geol. Assoc.*, **73**, 219–43.

ANDERSON, F. W. 1962. Correlation of the Upper Purbeck Beds of England with the German Wealden. *Lpool. Manchr. Geol. J.*, **3**, 21–32.

ARCHIBALD, J. 1934. *Kentish Architecture as influenced by Geology.* Ramsgate.

ARKELL, W. J. 1933. *The Jurassic System in Great Britain.* Oxford.

BENSTED, W. H. 1862. Notes on the Geology of Maidstone. *Geologist*, **5**, 294–301, 324–41, 378–82, 447–50.

BLACK, M. 1953. The Constitution of Chalk (Report on lecture). *Proc. Geol. Soc.*, No. 1499, lxxxi-vi.

BRITISH MUSEUM (NATURAL HISTORY). 1959. *British Caenozoic Fossils (Tertiary and Quaternary).* London.

—— 1962. *British Mesozoic Fossils.* London.

BURR, M. 1909. The South Eastern Coalfield: its Discovery and Development. *Sci. Progr.*, **3**, 379–409.

BURY, H. 1910. The Denudation of the Western End of the Weald. *Quart. J. Geol. Soc.*, **66**, 640–92.

CASEY, R. 1960–4. A Monograph of the Ammonoidea of the Lower Greensand. pts. 1–5, *Palaeontogr. Soc.*

—— 1961. The Stratigraphical Palaeontology of the Lower Greensand. *Palaeontology*, **3**, 487–621.

—— 1963. The Dawn of the Cretaceous Period in Britain. *Bull. S.E. Union Sci. Soc.*, No. 117.

CLOET, R. L. 1954. A Hydrographic Analysis of the Goodwin Sands. *Geog. J.*, **120**, 203–15.

DE SITTER, L. U. 1956. *Structural Geology.* London.

DEWEY, H., WOOLDRIDGE, S. W., CORNES, H. W. and BROWN, E. E. S. 1925. Geology of the Canterbury District. *Proc. Geol. Assoc.*, **36**, 257–84.

DINES, H. G. 1945. Report of the Geological Survey in *Kent Coalfield Regional Survey Report: Ministry of Fuel and Power*, 7–25.

EDMUNDS, F. H. 1923. The Scenery of the Wealden Area in Relation to Geology. *S. East. Nat.*, **38**, 66–81.

FALCON, N. L. and KENT, P. E. 1960. Geological Results of Petroleum Exploration in Britain 1945–57. *Mem. Geol. Soc., London*, No. 2.

FAREY, J. 1806. MS. *Geological Section of the Country from London to Brighton.*

FERGUSON, J. C. 1926. The Geology of the country around Horsham. *Proc. Geol. Assoc.*, **37**, 401–13.

FOSTER, C. LE NEVE and TOPLEY, W. 1865. On the Superficial Deposits of the Valley of the Medway. *Quart. J. Geol. Soc.*, **21**, 443–74.

FOWLER, J. 1932. ' One Hundred Foot ' Raised Beach between Arundel and Chichester, Sussex. *Quart. J. Geol. Soc.*, **88,** 84–99.

GASTER, C. T. A. 1929. Chalk Zones in the Neighbourhood of Shoreham, Brighton and Newhaven. *Proc. Geol. Assoc.*, **40,** 328–40.

—— 1937–51. The Stratigraphy of the Chalk of Sussex. pts. 1–4, *Proc. Geol. Assoc.*, **48,** 356–73; **50,** 510–26; **55,** 173–88; **62,** 31–64.

GEORGE, T. N. 1962. Tectonics and Palaeogeography in Southern England. *Sci. Progr.*, **50,** 192–217.

GIGNOUX, M. 1955. *Stratigraphic Geology.* English translation by Woodford, G. G. from fourth French edition. San Francisco.

GODWIN-AUSTEN, R. A. C. 1856. On the Possible Extension of Coal Measures beneath the South Eastern part of England. *Quart. J. Geol. Soc.*, **12,** 38–73.

GOSSLING, F. 1929. The Geology of the Country around Reigate. *Proc. Geol. Assoc.*, **40,** 197–259.

GREEN, J. F. N. and OTHERS. 1934. The River Mole: its Physiography and Superficial Deposits. *Proc. Geol. Assoc.*, **45,** 35–69.

GULLIVER, F. P. 1897. Dungeness Foreland. *Geog. J.*, **9,** 536–46.

HAYWARD, H. A. 1932. The Geology of the Lower Greensand in the Dorking–Leith Hill District. *Proc. Geol. Assoc.*, **43,** 1–31.

HOLLINGWORTH, S. E., TAYLOR, J. H. and KELLAWAY, G. A. 1944. Large-scale Superficial Structures in the Northampton Ironstone Field. *Quart. J. Geol. Soc.*, **100,** 1–35.

HOPKINS, W. 1845. On the Geological Structure of the Wealden District and of the Bas Boulonnais. *Trans. Geol. Soc.* (2), **7,** 1–51.

HOWITT, F. 1964. The Stratigraphy and Structure of the Purbeck Inliers of Sussex. *Quart. J. Geol. Soc.*, **119,** 77–114.

KERNEY, M. P. 1963. Late-Glacial Deposits on the Chalk of South-East England. *Phil. Trans.*, Ser. B., **246,** No. 730, 203–54.

KING, W. B. R. 1954. The Geological History of the English Channel. *Quart. J. Geol. Soc.*, **110,** 77–101.

KIRKALDY, J. F. 1932. The Geology of the Country around Hascombe. *Proc. Geol. Assoc.*, **43,** 127–51.

—— 1958. Geology of the Weald. *Geol. Assoc. Guides*, No. 29.

—— 1963. The Wealden and Marine Lower Cretaceous Beds of England. *Proc. Geol. Assoc.*, **74,** 127–46.

KNOWLES, L. and MIDDLEMISS, F. A. 1958. The Lower Greensand in the Hindhead Area of Surrey and Hampshire. *Proc. Geol. Assoc.*, **69,** 205–38.

LEES, G. M. and COX, P. T. 1937. The Geological Basis of the Present Search for Oil in Great Britain. *Quart. J. Geol. Soc.*, **93,** 156–94.

LEWIS, W. V. 1932. The Formation of Dungeness Foreland. *Geog. J.*, **30,** 309–24.

MANTELL, G. A. 1822. *The Fossils of the South Downs, or Illustrations of the Geology of Sussex*, London.

—— 1833. *The Geology of the South-East of England.* London.

MARTIN, E. C. 1938. The Littlehampton and Portsdown Chalk Inliers and their relation to the Raised Beaches of West Sussex. *Proc. Geol. Assoc.*, **49,** 198–212.

MARTIN, P. J. 1828. *A Geological Memoir on Part of Western Sussex.* London.

MILNER, H. B. 1923. The Geology of the Country around East Grinstead, Sussex. *Proc. Geol. Assoc.*, **34,** 283–300.

OAKLEY, K. P. 1963. Man the Toolmaker. *Brit. Mus.* (*Nat. Hist.*), 5th edit. London.

PETTIJOHN, F. J. 1957. *Sedimentary Rocks.* 2nd edit. New York.

PITCHER, W. S. and OTHERS. 1958. The London Region. *Geol. Assoc. Guides*, No. 30.

PRESTWICH, J. 1892. The Raised Beaches and ' Head ' or Rubble Drift of the South of England. *Quart. J. Geol. Soc.*, **48,** 263–343.

PRICE, F. G. H. 1874. On the Gault of Folkestone. *Quart. J. Geol. Soc.*, **30,** 342–68.

REEVES, J. W. 1948. Surface Problems in the Search for Oil in Sussex. *Proc. Geol. Assoc.*, **59,** 234–69.

REID, C. 1887. On the Origin of Dry Valleys and of Coombe Rock. *Quart. J. Geol. Soc.*, **43,** 364–73.

ROBINSON, A. H. W. and CLOET, R. L. 1953. Coastal Evolution in Sandwich Bay, *Proc. Geol. Assoc.*, **64,** 69–82.

ROWE, A. W. 1900. The Zones of the White Chalk of the English Coast. *Proc. Geol. Assoc.*, **16,** 289–368.

SCHUBERT, A. R. 1957. *History of the British Iron and Steel Industry.* London.

SPATH, L. F. 1923. Excursion to Folkestone, with notes on the Zones of the Gault. *Proc. Geol. Assoc.*, **34,** 70–6.

—— 1923–43. A Monograph of the Ammonoidea of the Gault. pts. 1–16, *Palaeontogr. Soc.*

STAMP, L. D. 1921. On Cycles of Sedimentation in the Eocene Strata of the Anglo-Franco-Belgium Basin. *Geol. Mag.*, **63,** 108–14, 146–57, 194–200.

STEERS, J. A. 1948. *The Coastline of England and Wales.* Cambridge.

STRAHAN, A. 1913. Anniversary Address of the President. *Quart. J. Geol. Soc.*, **69,** liv-xci.

STRAKER, E. 1931. *Wealden Iron.* London.

STUBBLEFIELD, C. J. and TRUEMAN, A. E. 1946. The Faunal Sequence in the Kent Coalfield. *Geol. Mag.*, **83,** 266–79.

—— *in* Trueman, A. E. 1954. *The Coalfields of Britain.* London, 154–66.

SWEETING, G. S. 1930. Geological Structure of the Ashburnham, Battle and Crowhurst District. *Proc. Geol. Assoc.*, **41,** 44–52.

TAITT, A. H. and KENT, P. E. 1958. *Deep Boreholes at Portsdown* (*Hants*) *and Henfield* (*Sussex*). London.

TAYLOR, J. H. 1963. Sedimentary Features of an Ancient Deltaic Complex: the Wealden Rocks of Southeastern England. *Sedimentology*, **2,** 2–28.

WHITAKER, W. 1866. On the ' Lower London Tertiaries ' of Kent. *Quart. J. Geol. Soc.*, **22,** 404–35.

WHITE, G. 1789. *The Natural History and Antiquities of Selbourne* (Numerous later editions).

WILLS, L. J. 1951. *A Palaeogeographic Atlas of the British Isles and Adjacent Parts of Europe.* London.

WOOLDRIDGE, S. W. and GOLDRING, F. 1953. *The Weald.* London.
—— and LINTON, D. L. 1955. *Structure, Surface and Drainage in South-East England.* 2nd edit., London.
ZEUNER, F. E. 1959. *The Pleistocene Period.* 2nd edit., London.

# Index

Printed in England for Her Majesty's Stationery Office by Commercial Colour Press London E.7
Dd.595759 K40 11/78

## List of Handbooks on the Regional Geology of Great Britain

**England and Wales**

| | |
|---|---:|
| Northern England (*4th Edition,* 1971) . . . . . | 40p |
| London and Thames Valley (*3rd Edition,* 1960) . . | 40p |
| Central England (*3rd Edition,* 1969) . . . . . | 40p |
| East Yorkshire and Lincolnshire (1948) . . . | 45p |
| The Welsh Borderland (*3rd Edition,* 1971) . . . | 40p |
| South-West England (*4th Edition,* 1975) . . . | 70p |
| Hampshire Basin and Adjoining Areas (*3rd Edition,* 1960) . | 95p |
| East Anglia and Adjoining Areas (*4th Edition,* 1961) . | 80p |
| South Wales (*3rd Edition,* 1970) . . . . | 50p |
| North Wales (*3rd Edition,* 1961) . . . . | £1.30 |
| The Pennines and Adjacent Areas (*3rd Edition,* 1954) . | £1.20 |
| Bristol and Gloucester District (*2nd Edition,* 1948) . . | £1.20 |

**Scotland**

| | |
|---|---:|
| Grampian Highlands (*3rd Edition,* 1966) . . . | £1.75 |
| Northern Highlands (*3rd Edition,* 1960) . . . | 37p |
| South of Scotland (*3rd Edition,* 1971) . . . . . | 50p |
| Midland Valley of Scotland (*2nd Edition,* 1948) . . | £1.50 |
| Tertiary Volcanic Districts (*3rd Edition,* 1961) . . | £1.00 |
| Orkney and Shetland (1976) . . . . . . | £2.25 |

*The above prices do not include postage*

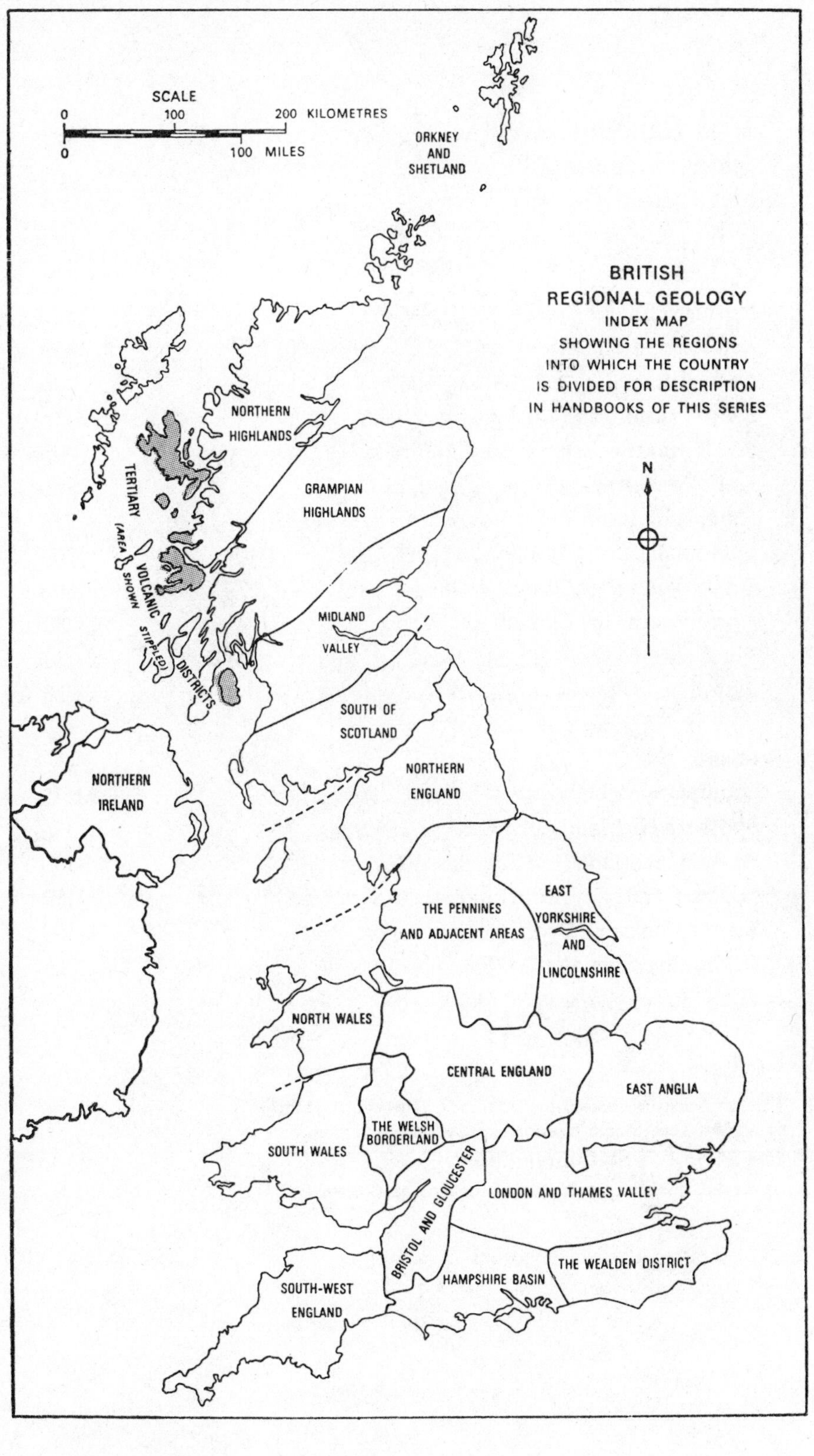

SCALE
0
100
200 KILOMETRES
0
100 MILES
ORKNEY
AND
SHETLAND
BRITISH
REGIONAL GEOLOGY
INDEX MAP
SHOWING THE REGIONS
INTO WHICH THE COUNTRY
IS DIVIDED FOR DESCRIPTION
IN HANDBOOKS OF THIS SERIES
N
NORTHERN
HIGHLANDS
TERTIARY
VOLCANIC
DISTRICTS
(AREA SHOWN STIPPLED)
GRAMPIAN
HIGHLANDS
MIDLAND
VALLEY
SOUTH OF
SCOTLAND
NORTHERN
IRELAND
NORTHERN
ENGLAND
THE PENNINES
AND ADJACENT AREAS
EAST
YORKSHIRE
AND
LINCOLNSHIRE
NORTH WALES
CENTRAL ENGLAND
EAST ANGLIA
THE WELSH
BORDERLAND
SOUTH WALES
BRISTOL AND GLOUCESTER
LONDON AND THAMES VALLEY
THE WEALDEN DISTRICT
HAMPSHIRE BASIN
SOUTH-WEST
ENGLAND